# BROKEN DECEPTION

## JEANETTE BURNS

Published 2023 by Your Book Angel
Copyright © Jeanette Burns

The characters are all mine, any similarities with other fictional or real persons/places are coincidental.

Printed in the United States
Edited by Keidi Keating
Layout by Rochelle Mensidor

ISBN: 979-8-9876155-7-7

# PROLOGUE

In a place where a gunshot or a scream went ignored, two people ran down the street to avoid the two men chasing them. Up ahead, a carriage was waiting to aid them in their escape. However, the men were gaining on them fast.

The driver caught sight of them and hollered at the footman to open the door. As they reached the door, what looked like a young boy never slowed down as he sailed inside the carriage to immediately turn and help the footmen get a woman in quickly. Seeing the pursuers closing in, the driver hit the horses with the reins before the footman could shut the door. As the footman stepped up on the side, one of the men reached and grabbed the door. Before he could enter, the footmen kicked him square in the chest, sending him flying back and hitting the ground.

"Bloody hell," said the man lying on the ground.

Feagin Parnell stood there, looking in the direction the carriage had vanished, rage evident on his face. "You will regret running away from me," he said through gritted teeth.

"Boss, what do we do now?" said the man still on the ground.

"We find her," he replied.

"How? We have never seen that boy's face. We do not know who sent him. All I know is he was fast." The man sat up, grunting from being kicked.

"He got word somehow. How else did he know where to come to get her? Someone told, and I will find out who, even if I have to kill a few whores to do it." Feagin turned to walk back, stopped, and looked at the man on the ground.

"Murray, get up. You are embarrassing yourself." He shook his head, wondering why he kept him around. A large scar ran from Feagin's nose across his left cheek. Nobody knew how he got it, but it served to keep most folks away. He wasn't your typical crime boss. The wealthy peerage protected Feagin. They either had business with him, or he used blackmail. Either way, he was untouchable.

"I will find out who that bastard is and enjoy killing him slowly," he said with a smile.

As the men walked away, Murray stopped and looked back. He had a sad look in his eyes briefly, but then he smiled and continued walking away.

Across town, in a very wealthy district, a carriage pulled behind a townhouse. Waiting, there was a man and woman who appear to be servants. Once the carriage stopped, the footman opened the door, and the woman in the cloak stepped out, revealing a child, about a year old, in her arms.

"Amy, welcome to your new home. I am Clare, and this is Elliot."

"I am to live here?" Amy asked as she stared at the huge house.

"Yes, can you cook or sew?" Clare asked.

"I can cook; my mother taught me."

"Excellent, we now have a cook." Clare smiled.

The person inside the carriage tapped the roof, letting the driver know it was time to go. Amy turned to look at the carriage.

"God bless you," she whispered

'Let us get you and the wee one inside. What is his name?" Clare asked.

"John."

They continued to chat as they walked inside.

Elliot watched the carriage leave, wondering how long their luck would hold before something terrible happened.

# CHAPTER ONE

Broken bones can heal,
but the wound a word
opens can fester forever.

Jessamyn West

Atherton Hall was at a full peak with people dancing and talking, but most were trying to curry favor. It was the most popular social event of the season. Everyone wanted an invite to the Atherton ball. Well, almost everyone. Veronica Aldridge desperately wished to be anywhere but there.

You couldn't say she was a wallflower, even though she tried to hide the whole time. This season was so different from her first. She could remember how excited and hopeful she'd been—shopping for the perfect dresses, having her hair curled and pinned, even having her face made. But it didn't take long for reality to sink in when she got a good taste of the cruel ton and their daughters. Finally, giving up, she completely changed. Her beautiful, long blonde hair in a tight bun, her dresses so plain and modest, you would mistake her for a governess. If only her mother would give up and stop making her attend social functions. The only thing she now enjoyed at those events was being completely invisible.

Of course, it helped that she was in a corner behind a huge, horrible monstrosity of a vase. She wasn't sure if people didn't see her or just didn't care, but she'd heard more gossip than anyone should. She listened to who wanted to marry whom, people conducting business, and even some intimate details that confused her. At least tonight, nobody talked about her.

Being the daughter of the wealthy Lord Henry Aldridge, Marquess of Cambridge, made life difficult. Gentlemen were constantly harassing her. It wasn't because she was beautiful. She wasn't. It was her ungodly large dowry. Veronica was considered plain looking, unlike her friends, who were beyond beautiful. She stood five-two with a curvy figure, which she hid. But she had the prettiest sky-blue eyes. Those that knew her saw an inner beauty incomparable to anyone else.

Needing some fresh air, she stepped out on the terrace. Most girls would not dare be outside alone, but everyone feared her father. Those who thought of compromising his children would meet with disaster. On the other hand, no one could question his love for his children. She couldn't help but smile when she thought of her father. Still not taking any chances, she never went too far alone.

Veronica wanted to get married, but the only ones offering were desperate fortune hunters. Her father didn't care if she married or not. He was willing to do whatever she wanted. Sometimes she thought he would be happy if she spent the rest of her life living with him.

As Veronica stood enjoying the cool night's breeze, she heard a voice behind some bushes. Quietly, she moved closer so she could hear better. She froze when she heard her name.

"Veronica Aldridge, why her? Do you really want to marry her?" asked a male voice.

"Bloody hell no, but for eighty thousand pounds, I would marry my horse."

A roar of laughter hurt her, but she already knew everyone came calling for her because of the dowry.

"Her father refused. I informed him he was lucky anybody called for her. Could you imagine bedding her? You would have to close your eyes and think of something else. Maybe my horse." Laughter erupted.

"That is what a mistress is for. Once you have an heir, you do not have to tolerate sharing a bed with her again," said someone with a chuckle.

Tears stung her eyes as she listened to some very disgusting comments about the way she looked. She felt the need to run but stopped when she saw someone standing close. Owen Pierce, her friend Dinah's brother. She lowered her head, embarrassed, for she knew he had heard.

He walked over to her and held out his arm for her to take. She slowly raised her hand to his arm, letting him lead her back to the ball. She stopped right outside the door.

"It is best if we do not walk in together," she said.

"Why?" he asked, confused.

"I do not want people to get the wrong impression. You know how the ton likes to gossip. You should not be seen with me." She held her head up, acting like it didn't bother her.

"Do not let what those half-wits say get to you. Unfortunately, some tend to resort to degrading others to ease their own embarrassment," Owen said, looking at her.

She looked at him and just stared. If only she were as beautiful as he was handsome. Owen was tall and muscular, with raven black hair, blue-green eyes that reminded her of the sea, and a deep voice that made her feel warm.

"Thank you for the kind words, my lord." She softly curtsied and walked away.

Veronica moved through the crowd looking for her mother, concentrating on her breathing to keep from crying. It was something she'd learned to do during her first season to keep what pride she had left intact. All she wanted was to get out of there, climb into her bed and forget about tonight. Spotting her mother, she started walking towards her, but she stopped when she heard her name again.

"Lady Ellen, has Veronica had any more offers?" asked Lady Worthington. She was a member of the ton who could decide if a girl's season went smoothly or if it ended quickly.

*Why can't they find someone else to talk about?* thought Veronica.

"Yes, but her father has refused another. I do not know what he is thinking."

"It is a shame she favors Leah," said Lady Worthington

The other women seemed stunned by the comment. Leah was Veronica's birth mother. She died when Veronica was an infant, leaving her and her four-year-old brother, Ellis. Lord Aldridge married Ellen when Veronica was three. She could tell Ellen was getting upset when she saw her shoulders pull back.

*Time to go,* she thought.

"Mother!" she said softly.

Lady Ellen turned quickly with a surprised look. "Ronnie." She used the nickname her family and friends called her.

"Can we go home? I am not feeling well."

The other women looked and turned quickly, knowing she had heard the comment about Leah.

"Yes, of course," turning back to the women, she added, "Excuse us."

"Certainly," said Lady Worthington; the rest nodded.

They made their way outside and called for their carriage, not saying a word until they had settled in and on their way.

"What happened?" she asked, looking at Veronica.

"I need to ask you something. Please do not answer as a mother who loves me and wants to protect me from being hurt."

"I will try." Ellen swallowed, worried about where the conversation was going.

"I know that I am not beautiful. I accepted that a long time ago. But, mum, am I so ugly that men must close their eyes to be with me?"

Her mother sat next to her and pulled her into her arms. "Heavens, no," Ellen said, causing Veronica to lose her composure.

Within seconds, she was sobbing uncontrollably. Ellen held her and rubbed her back as when Veronica was a little girl. She might not have given birth to her, but she loved her as if she had, and she would move heaven and earth to protect her.

After a while, she straightened Ronnie up and dried her tears with her gloved hands. "That is absurd; why would you ask that?"

Veronica took a deep breath, trying to control her crying. "I heard some men talking outside tonight. Mum, why do I have to look like this? Why could I not have come from you?" she said, sobbing again.

"Listen to me. You are elegant, graceful, and lovely. If men cannot see that, then they are not worthy of you." Ellen paused as she looked at Veronica's face, remembering her good friend. "Ronnie, your mother loved you with all her heart and deserves your respect. Do not ever say that again," she said, firmly.

"I'm sorry," Veronica replied, lowering her head.

"Is this why you have changed the way you look? Have there been other comments you never told me about?" Ellen asked.

Veronica lowered her head." Some of the girls told me they had heard how ugly my mother had been. They overheard their parents talking about how much I looked like her. Most of the time, they would point and laugh when I walked by. Some said it was useless even to try to look pretty. My father has put enough in my dowry. He will buy me a husband."

Ellen didn't know what to say. By that time, they had returned home, and the footman had opened the carriage door. After stepping out, she told her to go upstairs, bathe, and go to bed.

As they reached the door, it opened, and their butler, Railbert, stood there, waiting to help them. After removing her cloak and gloves, she went upstairs without a word. Railbert knew something was wrong. He came from Scotland with Leah when she married Henry and was very close to both of her children.

"Where is my husband?"

"In his study, milady."

Ellen walked hurriedly to his study but stopped and knocked softly from outside, waiting for an answer.

"Come in." Railbert stopped and watched her open the door. "Ah, my love, you are back early," Henry said.

"We need to talk," Railbert heard her say as she shut the door. He turned and walked away, wondering if they have finally realized what has been happening to Ronnie.

# CHAPTER TWO

It's amazing how complete
is the delusion that beauty
is goodness

Leo Tolstoy

O wen made it home around eleven, surprised to see a light inside his father's study. He knocked and opened the door. "Father," he said.

Calum Pierce, Earl of Westridge, had his head buried in paperwork. Finally, he looked up. "Oh, Owen, I did not hear you come in."

"What is wrong?" Owen asked as he walked toward his father.

Calum sat back, looking tired. "It is time we talk. Take a seat."

Owen sat in a chair facing the desk, looking at his father, knowing something wasn't right.

"I was hoping to be able to correct this before things got worse," Calum said.

"Correct what?" Owen asked, worriedly.

"Our ship, the Maybeck, sunk on its way back."

Owen's face paled. *Not good,* he thought.

"You know, it was our most valuable shipment and now our most significant loss. I was able to pay the investors back, but it took everything we had." He paused. I thought I could recoup faster, but I haven't been able to. A friend has been loaning funds to keep things going and to keep people from finding out we are threadbare."

"What can I do?" asked Owen.

"You have been doing excellent handling the country estate. It has been self-sufficient for some time now. We might be going back there sooner than planned."

"Things are that bad?" Owen asked, rubbing his forehead.

"Yes, son, they are." Calum lowered his head.

"Does mother know?"

"I told her yesterday. She took Dinah to a friend's house instead of Atherton's ball tonight. I do not even have her dowry anymore." He seemed utterly defeated.

"There has to be something we can do?"

"I am afraid it will take time and a bit of luck. Right now, I need you to keep handling the estate. We might close this place and let go of the staff. That is the last resort."

After a while, Owen left the study, going to his room. He lay in bed, unable to sleep, trying to think of a way to save his family.

The following day, he got up and dressed, though things felt different. Overnight, his world changed. He sent word to Ada Claridge, the Earl of Kingsley's daughter, that he needed to see her, and she needed to be alone. He had been courting Ada for some time and was preparing to make an offer to her father. Now, he was not so sure.

Ada stared at Owen as they rode in the carriage, knowing something was wrong. Owen was always smiling and talkative, but not today. Getting a little uneasy by his change in behavior, she snuggled up to him and placed her head on his shoulder.

"What is wrong?" she asked.

Taking a deep breath, he turned and looked at her. "I need to talk to you about something that has happened."

He hesitated, not knowing how to start. As he stared, he thought about how beautiful she was, with chestnut hair, big brown eyes, small but well-rounded body. Would she run away from him when he tells her?

"My family has had some issues lately. We had a ship sink with a considerable amount of cargo. It puts us in a financial situation," he said nervously.

"How bad?"

"Bad. We do not have anything left. I have been trying to think of a solution."

"Would my dowry help?" she asked, thinking that might be her chance to get him to marry her. When Ada wanted something, she got it, and she wanted Owen.

"No, we need a substantial amount of money. I am sorry. I know this is unexpected, so I will understand if you want to end things now," he said, looking away.

"Oh no, Owen, you know how I feel about you. That hasn't changed," Ada said sweetly.

He hugged her tightly, thinking how lucky he was to have someone like her in his life.

After he took her home, she went upstairs, slammed her door, and started breaking everything in sight. All the staff shuddered and hurried away, afraid of being in her path.

Ada's mother, Lady Agnes, entered her room when she heard the commotion. "What is wrong, Ada?"

"You are not going to believe, after all my hard work, he ends up without a shilling to his name," she screamed, sitting on the floor like a child.

"What is this nonsense your spouting?" Agnes asked.

"Owen just informed me his family is penniless. One of their ships sank somewhere, and now everything is ruined," she spat.

"How can that be? Tell me everything that he said," Agnes said, shocked.

After she related the conversation, Agnes sat there, thinking. Agnes was well known for her cunning ways. A member of the ton and one of those women who found pleasure in causing others pain. Over the years, a few girls had their reputations ruined by her vicious rumors.

"If only my dowry were as large as Veronica's, I would have Owen right where I want him. Did you know that the enormous townhouse on Broad Street is a part of her dowry? That ugly clot doesn't deserve to have everything. It is not fair," Ada shrieked as she plopped down in a chair.

After a few minutes, Agnes looked at Ada with a smile. "I have a way of solving this. I need you to stay quiet and listen to what I say."

After a while, Ada says, "Perfect, that will ruin her."

# CHAPTER THREE

Kind words are like honey,
sweet to the soul and
health to the body

proverbs

Veronica sat in bed, watching her maid Lydia prepare her clothes for the day, reviewing everything that happened last night—deciding no more tea parties and no more balls. If only she could convince her mother and father that her season was over.

*Maybe they will let me go to the country,* she thought.

"How was your night?" Lydia asked.

Usually, Veronica confided in her about everything, but she couldn't bring herself to speak about last night. "Normal, as always."

After dressing, she went downstairs to get something to eat. As she entered the dining room, she noticed her parents were at the table.

"Good morning, Ronnie," said Henry.

"Good morning," she replied with a smile.

"How did you sleep?" asked Ellen.

"I slept great." She filled her plate.

Sitting across from Ellen, she started eating. Henry and Ellen glanced at each other. To everyone, it seemed as if last night had never happened.

After a while, Henry stood. "Ronnie, come to my study when you are finished." He then picked up the newspaper and left the dining room.

"What does he want to talk to me about?"

"He just wants to talk about some things."

"If it is about last night, there is no need. I am quite all right."

Ellen watched her for a few minutes. "You cannot keep doing that," she said.

"Doing what?"

"Pretending everything is all right. It is not good keeping things like this inside and not talking to us."

Veronica was quiet and continued to eat.

After they finished, Ellen left, and Veronica started helping clean the dining room. Henry disapproved of her helping the staff, but she kept doing it, and he pretended he didn't know.

Most of the servants have worked for Henry all her life. Several of them, besides Railbert, came with Leah from Scotland. As they worked, they would tell her stories of her mother.

Once finished, she went to her father's study, softly knocked, and walked in.

"Have a seat," Henry said as he arranged some papers.

Veronica stared at him. At least she had his blonde hair and blue eyes. She couldn't help but be jealous of her brother Ellis, for he had gotten their father's good looks. She lowered her head, mad at herself for wishing for something that cannot be.

*You are ugly and will always be ugly,* she thought.

"I need to tell you about your mother and me," he says as he walks around his desk and comes to sit beside her. "There are things I never wanted you to know, and I hope it does not change how you feel toward me," he says, looking at her.

"Father, nothing you say could change how much I love you."

Henry took a deep breath and let it out slowly. "When I was young, I lived an unruly, scandalous, decadent lifestyle. My father was not an affectionate, loving man. He cared only for prestige and coins. Doing almost anything to further his wealth. One day, he came across this mill, which had extensive property, and he wanted it."

"I know that is how you met her. Grandfather Brannon sold it to him cheap with the condition that you marry his daughter," she said.

"Yes. I refused at first, but my father threatened to disinherit me. I knew he would do it, and I enjoyed the life wealth had given me, so I married her, but I was a horrible husband, Ronnie. When I would come home, which was rare, I was normally tanked. I was cruel and hateful, never saying a kind word to her. It got so bad, she would never look at me, always keeping her eyes down. And yet, never a cross word left her lips. She took my cruelty. I was so angry my father had forced me to marry, and I took it out on her."

As Henry continued to talk, Veronica could see the pain in his eyes.

"Then I got really sick. I had a high fever for days. Every time I would wake, Leah was there. For two weeks, she took constant care of me. Once I got better, I tried to sit up and eat, but I was so weak, I could barely lift my arms. She started feeding me.

"I asked her why she was helping me, after how mean I had been to her. She should have left my care to the servants. What if she had gotten sick and died?" Henry paused for a few seconds, taking a deep breath. "She said that would have solved both our problems. That's when I realized what an arse I had been to her. She thought I would be glad if she died.

"After that, I started coming home at a decent hour and spending time with her. It was initially awkward, but eventually, we started getting to know one another.

"One day at supper, my business manager came in very excited. It turned out, while I was acting a fool, Leah had been handling my business affairs. She had made some very lucrative purchases; quite a bit of our wealth was due to her. She had an excellent eye for business.

"Then she had Ellis. I still remember that day, so afraid I would lose her. Somewhere along the way, I fell in love with my wife. Then you came along, and I was so happy." He paused for a second, and Veronica looked at him, noticing a tear falling down his cheek.

"Out of nowhere, she got sick. I held her hand and told her how much I loved her." He paused to gain control as his tears fell. "She thanked me for giving her such a wonderful life and showing her what it felt like to be loved. Then she was gone."

Veronica wrapped her arms around him, and they cried together.

After a while, she pulled back. "Why did you tell me this?"

"Because someone is going to see what a wonderful, lovely, incredible person you are. Never stop believing there will be someone to love you as much as I loved your mother. I am sorry if running off all those men has made things difficult for you. Ronnie. But you will always be my little girl, and I will not let anybody marry you."

She gave him another hug and kissed his cheek.

"Thank you, father," she said with a teary smile.

"Now, dry those tears and go enjoy the rest of your day," he said with a smile. After she left, he got up and walked to the window. He said a silent prayer that his little girl could find the love that she deserves without the heartache her mother went through. Not knowing that at the same time, people were making plans that would destroy her.

# CHAPTER FOUR

The art of pleasing is
the art of deceiving

Luc De Clapier

The next morning, Lady Ann, Owen's mother, received an invitation to tea from Agnes Claridge. Had Owen already told Ada? Did Agnes want to humiliate her in person?

"What is wrong?" Owen asked as he noticed her standing there with a pale face.

"I received an invite from Agnes. Did you tell Ada what has happened?

"Yes, I have. She was very understanding and did not want to stop seeing me. So do not worry about it. Maybe she just wants to assure you that nothing has changed?"

"You are probably right," she replied, still nervous.

Ann never forgot what it was like for her when she had her coming out. She'd been treated horribly by Agnes and the other girls because her father was a simple merchant. Once she married Calum, things changed, and she was considered one of them. To become an outcast again was her biggest fear. She would do anything to prevent that.

When she arrived at Agnes's door, she hesitated. Taking a deep breath, she knocked.

"May I help you?" asked a well-dressed butler.

"Lady Pierce to see Lady Agnes."

He stepped back and let Ann walk inside. She removed her cloak and gloves.

"I'll inform her you have arrived," he said as he left.

She stood in the foyer, admiring the décor and noticing all the staff were exceptionally well dressed. The Claridge townhouse was a perfect example of wealth.

*What will I do if we lose everything?* she thought.

"This way, my lady."

As she entered the sitting room, she noticed Agnes was already there.

"Please, take a seat," said Agnes, motioning to the couch across from her.

"How have you been?" Ann asked.

"Quite well."

There was silence while Agnes poured Ann a cup of tea.

"You must be wondering why I invited you today. Let me first say, you do not have to worry about me saying anything about your financial difficulties to anyone. I want to help. I believe I have a solution to your problem." Agnes took a sip of tea.

"Oh?"

"I have thought about Owen marrying Ada for her dowry, but he informed her it would not be enough. He would have to marry someone else. Someone like Veronica Aldridge." She paused, waiting to see if Ann understood.

"I am not sure I understand this correctly. You think Owen should marry Veronica for her dowry? Granted, it would solve our problem, but what about Ada?"

"Ada is very taken with Owen, and I believe he feels the same about her. That is why he would not stay married to Veronica. After an appropriate amount of time has passed, he will divorce her."

Ann was speechless at first. "That would ruin her. And let us not forget what Henry Aldridge is capable of doing."

"Yes, that is why we will have to have a good reason for the divorce. It is quite simple to cause a situation where a man would divorce his wife. Let us also not forget Henry is extremely wealthy, and there would be someone desperate enough to overlook the situation, and she could remarry."

"Have you talked to Ada about this?"

"Yes, I have. She would agree, as long as she is assured it is only temporary. Ada is a very understanding and considerate child."

Ann already knew what kind of person Ada was, but she could only agree with Agnes. Ann was only okay with Owen courting her to ensure her station in society. Being a part of the Claridge family guaranteed protection.

"You just have to convince Owen."

"I do not know if that is possible. Owen is very noble and would be against deceiving and using Veronica."

"These are dire times, Ann. Sacrifices must be made." Agnes pauses and takes a sip of tea. It seems her whole demeanor changed before she continued to speak. "At this point, I cannot approve of them being together. I would hate to see how others would react when they hear of our sudden refusal of Owen courting Ada. Of course, we would have to explain the change," Agnes said, looking straight into Ann's eye.

The threat was clear. Owen does it, or Agnes ruins her family.

"I will convince him this is the only way. I am sure he will agree, especially where Ada is concerned," Ann replied, trying to seem confident.

"Good, then we agree. I look forward to hearing the news of their engagement."

Ann stands, eager to get away from Agnes. "I should be getting back. I need to speak to Owen immediately. The faster we get this in motion, the quicker we can repair our position." Ann nodded as she left the room.

After entering the carriage, she put her head back and closed her eyes. *What am I going to do? How do I convince Owen to do this? I will not become a social pariah,* she thought.

Once she arrived home, she told the butler to inform Owen she needed to see him as soon as he returned. She then went to her room and thought about what to say to make Owen marry Veronica. Ann was desperate, and Veronica's life didn't matter anymore.

# CHAPTER FIVE

No one is useless in this
world who lightens the
burdens of others

Charles Dickens

Three girls were coming out of a shop, talking, and laughing. If someone were to describe them, they would say there were no three people so different.

Veronica had light blonde hair, sky-blue eyes, and pale skin. She wore a light yellow dress with pastel flowers embroidered on the hem and white ribbons around her waist and tied in her hair.

Dinah Pearce, daughter of Callum Pierce, Earl of Westridge, with her raven black hair and blue-green eyes like her brother. She wore a dark blue dress with lace around the neck and sleeves and a light blue ribbon around her waist tied into a bow.

Finally was Hannah Corbin, daughter of Viscount Archie Corbin, who had dark red hair, big green eyes, and a few freckles on her nose. She wore an emerald dress with yellow roses embroidered down the center and along the hem, with yellow ribbons around her waist and in her hair.

They were completely opposite in looks, but you would not find anyone more loyal to each other than those three. Being tired from shopping, they decided on a tea shop right around the corner to rest and chat for a while.

Finding a secluded table, they sat down and ordered.

"You start, Hannah. How have you been? Has Oliver been calling still?" Veronica asked.

"Things have been okay," Hannah answered, not looking up from her tea.

Veronica looked at Hannah and Dinah, noticing how uncomfortable they seemed. "Okay, ladies, don't do that."

"What?" they both reply innocently.

"Do not stop confiding in me because my situation does not look good. I need your friendship, not your pity. Do you not know how happy I would be for both of you to find love and get married? So, start talking," she says, looking at Hannah.

"Yes, he is still coming around. We went for a carriage ride the other day. He is so sweet and considerate. We had intense conversations where he asked me to be open and honest. He wants to know what I think. And does not want me to be a weak, brainless creature," she says with a big smile that does not reach her eyes, and Veronica knows why. Hannah has someone else in her heart.

"That's fantastic. I am happy for you." Veronica smiled.

"Me too," said Dinah.

"Okay, it is your turn. Who has come to call this week?" Veronica asked Dinah.

"Johnathan Tisdale came by with flowers," Dinah said but looked down, not smiling.

"What's wrong?" Hannah asked.

Dinah didn't say anything but started sobbing. Both girls moved to either side of her and wrapped their arms around her until she stopped crying.

"Talk to us. What has happened?" Veronica asked.

"It does not matter who comes to call for me. Once they find out what has happened, they will cry off," she said, wiping the tears from her face.

"What are you talking about?' asked Hannah.

"My family is ruined. We are penniless," she said, lowering her head.

Both Hannah and Veronica were speechless for a minute.

"How did this happen, and why have you not said anything?" asked Hannah.

"I wanted to, but I was embarrassed. I do not know all the details about how it happened. All I know is we are in trouble. Mother says father is trying to repair things." Both Veronica and Hannah stacked their hands on top of Dinah's, something they have always done to show unity between them. The gesture made Dinah cry again.

"You will always have us," said Hannah.

"Always," echoed Veronica.

"Thank you. I love you both so much," Dinah said, wiping her tears.

"Now we need to put our heads together and make some plans," said Veronica.

"Yes, starting with Johnathan. When he sends a request to visit, contact us, and we will set up a get-together at one of our houses. He, of course, will be invited, and you can spend time with him and not worry about him noticing anything at home," said Hannah.

The next hour went by with them making plans for their friend. Dinah could not have asked for better people in her life.

After the girls left the tea shop, they went their separate ways. Knowing why Dinah did not buy anything, Veronica returned to the dress shop. She ordered dresses, bonnets, gloves, and everything else a girl could need and arranged for them to be sent to Dinah's house when ready.

Veronica's friends meant everything to her. She would not allow them to suffer.

When she returned home, she went straight upstairs to the nursery where her four-year-old brother, Lucien, slept. She stared down at him, thankful that he was so beautiful. He had his mother's brown hair and his father's looks and blue eyes.

"You will be so handsome when you grow up. I will make sure you are protected and loved," she whispered to him as she stroked his soft hair. She didn't notice Ellen was standing in the doorway, listening. As Veronica turned, she stopped, seeing her mother standing there, smiling.

Ellen opened her arms, and she walked into them for a hug. They walked out of the room quietly, shutting the door.

"Did you know about the Pierce family?"

"Yes, your father told me."

"Is there something we can do to help?"

"You cannot tell anyone, but your father has been helping."

"Really? I am glad. Dinah told Hannah and me today. She is so upset. My heart breaks for her."

"You and Hannah need to keep quiet about this. If it gets around, they could lose everything they have left," Ellen said firmly.

"I understand."

"Good. Now, go get changed. Supper will be ready shortly."

"Okay, mother," Veronica said, walking towards her room.

As Ellen watched her leave, she couldn't help but hope for someone worthwhile to come into her life. God knew the girl deserved it.

Lydia was waiting for Veronica when she entered her room. "We got another message," she said.

"When?"

"Tonight."

"Tell Adrian and Ian to be ready," said Veronica.

"Yes, my Lady," Lydia said and left the room.

*It will be a long night,* Veronica thought as she walked to a chest at the foot of her bed. She removed everything from it, and at the bottom was a hidden compartment. She stared at the items briefly, then removed what looked like men's clothing, including a wide-brimmed hat.

# CHAPTER SIX

Deception is one of the
quickest ways to gain little
things and lose big things.

Thomas Sowell

When Owen returned home, he found his mother in the library staring at the fire with a solemn expression on her face.

"Mother, you needed to see me?"

"Oh, Owen. I did not hear you come in," she said, moving in her seat nervously.

"Is something wrong?"

"Please, come and sit. We need to talk," Ann replied, wiping her hand on her gown.

"What about?" he asked, noticing how uneasy she seemed.

"You have to marry Veronica Aldridge," she blurted, taking Owen by surprise.

"What?"

"Lady Agnes and I discussed it and decided that the only way we can solve our problem is for you to marry Veronica."

No one spoke for a few seconds.

"No, I'm marrying Ada. You know this," he replied firmly. *She cannot be serious,* he thought.

"No, son. You are not. Agnes will not allow it until we have restored our wealth. Marrying Veronica will do this. Then, once we are financially secure, she will allow you to marry Ada."

"Wait, I am to marry Veronica for her dowry, so I can marry Ada? That's ridiculous. How can I marry both women? I would have to divorce...." Owen paused when he realized their plan. "No, mother, I won't do that. I can't do that." He shook his head.

"If you don't, Agnes will openly refuse your courting of Ada and tell everyone of our situation. Think about what this will do to your father. Dinah will not be able to marry, and everyone will shun me. There is no other way," she starts raising her voice.

"What about Ada? She won't agree to this farce."

"But she has, under the understanding that it is temporary."

Owen was stunned. He couldn't believe Ada would let him marry someone else. *This cannot be happening,* he thought.

"I need to leave. I need to think." He gets up.

"Go and talk to Ada. See for yourself," Ann said as she watched him leave. She wished she had never agreed to him courting Ada. What she thought was going to be her protection could end up destroying her.

Before leaving home, he sent Ada a message to meet him.

Later, Owen sat in a carriage outside her house. *I can't do this. How can they expect me to do this? To marry Veronica, only to turn around and divorce her? Who does things like that? Not me,* he thought.

Ada enters, immediately going to Owen and hugging him tightly. He holds her, breathing in her perfume, trying to calm done.

She pulls back and looks at him. "Your mother told you?"

"Yes. You agreed to this?"

"We have no choice. My mother will not let us be together now."

"Ada, we just need time to fix this. I know we can handle this without involving me marrying someone else," Owen said, hoping she would see the reason.

"She is considering other offers now. She will hold off for a while if you agree to do this. It will show her how much you love me." She held the sides of his face and looked into his eyes. "Owen, please, I do not want to marry someone else. I love you, and I know you love me," she said as tears rolled down her face.

"I don't know if I can do this. How do I intentionally use someone like this?" he said, sinking back into his seat, feeling defeated.

"I have faith in you, Owen. You can do this for your family, for me, for us." Ada looked at him pleadingly.

"So, you're okay with me marrying Veronica? What about her? This will ruin her."

"I know, and I hate it. I truly do. But Veronica will eventually be okay. It is our only way to be together," Ada said, trying to seem bothered by hurting Veronica.

"I need to return home and speak to Mother."

"I know this will be difficult, but you can do this. I love you, Owen." She kissed him passionately.

"I must go before my mother finds out I am not in the house. I do not know if she will approve of me still seeing you. Please, save me."

"I will," he replied in a low voice, realizing he might have to do that.

Ada exited the carriage and watched it leave from inside the gate. As she stood with a smug smile on her face, her mother walked up behind her.

"How did it go?" Agnes asked.

"I am sure he is going to do it."

"Did you act as I instructed, weak and pathetic?"

"Yes, I was quite convincing.

They turned around and walked back into the house, feeling quite pleased with themselves.

Owen walks into the sitting room, finding his mother staring out the window.

"All right, how do I do this? How do I convince Henry I want to marry his daughter?" he asked, sitting across from her.

First, they decided not to tell Owen's father. Callum could never know their true intentions. Dinah would be sent to Ann's sisters' home in the country. News of the engagement would be kept from her until it would be too late to stop.

"How are we going to keep Henry from coming after us? You know how he is. Can you imagine what he will do to those who hurt his daughter?"

"Agnes is going to devise a plan to compromise her so you can divorce without taking the blame."

Owen couldn't believe they were even considering doing something like this to another person. That was more than he could stand to hear. He got up to leave, but his mother's words stopped him as he grabs the door handle.

"I am sorry, son, but sometimes we must make sacrifices."

He stands there for a few seconds. "It is just a shame Veronica is the lamb we are sacrificing," he said, then opened the door and left.

Ann lowered her head and closed her eyes.

"God, forgive me," she whispered.

After he left his mother, he sent his valet to deliver a message to Henry requesting a meeting for the next day. He sat in his bedroom, sipping a glass of bourbon by the fire. He still couldn't believe things had turned out like that. However, it didn't take long to get a response from Henry.

Tomorrow morning at eleven.

After he read the message, he crumpled the letter and threw it in the fireplace. As he watched it burn, he thought, *I will lose my integrity, self-respect, and possibly my soul.*

That night, he drank until he passed out.

# CHAPTER SEVEN

We often shed tears
that deceive ourselves
after deceiving others

Fracois De La Rachefouch

The following day, Owen stayed in his room until it was time to leave for his meeting. He didn't want to see his mother or hear her say he had no choice. Dinah had already come to inform him; she was going to their aunt Miranda's to stay for a while. The lack of funds was a good excuse to get Dinah out of town.

As his valet, Edgar helped him dress. He seemed to notice Owen's depressed state.

"Sir, is everything good?"

"No, but it soon will be, I hope," he replied, quietly.

Once finished, he took one last look in the mirror. Then, he straightened his cravat and left his room.

As Owen sat in the carriage on the way, he started thinking about what his father would say if he found out. How would Dinah feel about him if she knew he was going to destroy her friend? He thought about turning the carriage around but remembered Ada's face and her tears. What else could he do? He couldn't let her marry another man.

It wasn't long before the carriage stopped, and the footman opened the door. He took a deep breath and exited.

After Owen entered the Aldridge home, he removed his hat and overcoat.

"I'll inform Lord Aldridge you have arrived," said Railbert.

As he waited, he reflected on the fact that he had known Henry all his life. They were members of the same club. Both of their families had occasionally celebrated holidays together, and now, he would deceive him and his family.

"This way, my lord," Railbert said, pulling him out of his trance.

"Good morning," said Owen as he entered Henry's office.

"Come in and take a seat. What did you wish to see me about?" asked Henry after Owen sat down.

"I would like to get your approval to start courting Veronica."

Henry sat back in his chair and tilted his head to the right as if he was sizing him up. "I was not expecting that." He leaned forward.

"I thought you were set on Kingsley's daughter?"

"That is not possible anymore."

"And my daughter is?" Henry asked, sounding skeptical.

"I know this seems sudden and strange, but I have thought quite a bit about this, and Veronica would make the perfect wife. She is kind and very intelligent. I've noticed how she treats everyone equally, no matter what their station in life is. She is unique."

"And her dowery has nothing to do with your decision?" Henry asked as he watched Owen to see if he would lie about his family's situation.

"I would be lying if I said it did not have some bearing on my decision. My family is in a bad situation, but to pick a wife to ease our case would be a huge mistake. I want a wife who can be my partner and help me with things, not one who only knows shopping and parties." Owen didn't have to lie about that. He truly wanted that in a wife.

For a few seconds, nothing was said. Henry thought about accepting Owen's offer. He was the exact type of man he wanted for his daughter. But it had come out of nowhere, and that bothered him.

"I need to go to White's to pick up something. Ride with me?" Henry said as he stood up. He wanted to see how he would react in public if it were known he wanted to marry Veronica.

"Of course," Owen said as he stood to follow him.

Two hours later, they returned, and he had made his decision. Owen seemed to have reacted to his satisfaction. After exiting the carriage, they stood in the courtyard, not going inside.

"I accept your proposal of courtship so long as Veronica agrees. I have faith she will make the right decision. Be open and honest with her."

"Is she home?"

"I am not sure. Come back later this evening for supper. Give Ellen and me some time to talk to her."

"I will. Thank you." Owen turns and leaves.

Henry enters the house, seeing Railbert just inside. "Where is my wife?"

"Library, I believe," Railbert answers as he takes his hat and overcoat.

He went straight there, where he found Ellen reading and Lucien on the floor playing.

"You will never believe what has happened," he said as he sat on the floor with his son.

"What, my love?" She put the book down.

"Owen has made an offer for Veronica." He looked up from his son to see how she would react.

Her smile immediately faded. "Say that again."

"Owen wants to marry her."

Ellen was quiet, not reacting at all.

"What do you think?" he asked, not being able to read her expression.

"I do not know what to think. Is it for the money?"

"He did not deny that was a part of his decision. I spent some time with him today. He seemed very sincere. I am still going to let Veronica make the final decision, so I have asked him to come for supper tonight. Where is Ronnie?"

"She has gone to the house on Broad's Street to check on things. I believe she has it fully staffed now. Maybe it is time to let her decide. I have always liked Owen. I just worry about how she will feel about this. He is very handsome. She will feel like she doesn't deserve him."

"We will sit her down as soon as she returns and talk to her. I do believe Owen could grow to have feelings for her," he says as he picks up Lucien and puts him on his lap.

"I pray he does," Ellen said, not so sure.

When Owen got home, his mother was waiting at the door.

"Well, how did it go?" she asked nervously.

"He has approved. Now I must convince Veronica," he said as he walked past her on his way upstairs.

"That should be easy. She would be a fool not to marry you," Ann said to Owen's back as he walked away.

Owen entered his bedroom, went straight to the cabinet, and poured a glass of port. He sat and sipped his drink, staring at nothing. The thought of facing Veronica and lying to her made him queasy. There was a soft knock on the door, which he ignored. It slowly opened, and he heard his mother.

"Owen, can I come in?"

"Yes," he said, taking a deep breath.

She walked in and shut the door but came no further. "Are you all right?"

"Does the sick feeling ever go away?" he asked, taking another sip, not looking at her.

Not knowing what to say, she just stood there.

"You do not have to worry. I will go ahead with the plan." He finished his drink in one gulp and stood up.

"I want to be alone. Please leave." His tone told her she should go. He couldn't stand to be around her right now. There was resentment growing in his heart.

After shutting the door, Ann leaned against it.

"He will be okay once this is over, and he returns with Ada. Then, everything will be back to normal," she said to herself, trying to ease her conscience. She then walked downstairs to wait for Callum to get home.

# CHAPTER EIGHT

You may be deceived if you
trust too much, but you will
live in torment if you don't
trust enough.

Frank Crane

Veronica got back to her home later than she had planned.

"Your father needs to speak to you," Railbert told her as she threw her cloak and gloves at him.

"I will see them after I change," she hollered back at him as she ran up the stairs. Getting the children she had saved settled into the orphanage had taken a while. The night didn't go as smoothly as expected. Thank God her brother had taught her how to fight since she was young. Ellis worried about her and wanted her to be strong, not a weak damsel. They had almost reached the carriage with five children and a woman when two men showed up unexpectedly. She and Aaron handled the two men as the rest made it to the carriage safely. Veronica was thankful; things could have gone so wrong.

After changing, she made her way down the stairs as Railbert opened the front door. She stopped, stunned that Owen was standing there, taking his gloves and overcoat off. He looked up to see Veronica standing on the stairs and started walking towards her.

Owen was somewhat surprised at her appearance. She wore a high-waisted peach-colored gown with puffy shoulder caps. The dress was low cut, showing a great deal of her breasts, and they weren't small. He wondered how she hid her figure when she was out in society. It was difficult for him not to look. His body was reacting, so he had to keep his eyes up. Her hair was pulled back and tied with peach-colored ribbons. A cascade of curls hung down past her waist. As he got closer, he noticed a small wisp of hair lying on her forehead.

He felt attracted to her and was uncomfortable with his reaction.

"Good evening, Lord Pierce. What a pleasant surprise," she said, smiling. Standing on the second step made her almost eye level with him and way too close for comfort. Her heart started beating faster as she looked at his gorgeous face.

"Your father invited me to dine with you tonight, so we can get to know one another." Veronica stood there confused, not knowing what to make of the situation. "Would you like to ride in the park with me tomorrow?"

She turned to look behind her to see if someone was there before slowly turning back to face him. "Me?" she asked, pointing to herself.

"Yes, you."

"Why would you want to go riding with me?"

"We need to get acquainted with each other. Also, we need to let people see us together before our engagement is made public."

Veronica stood there for a few seconds before she erupted into laughter.

Owen liked the sound of her laugh but wondered what was so funny.

"I never knew you had such a sense of humor," she said when she finally stopped laughing.

"I am not being humorous."

Her smile slowly fades. "Do you know what you are saying? I think you have become delusional. I need to get someone to check on you. Maybe a doctor?" She moved around him when he softly grabbed her arm to stop her. She was surprised at how warm his touch was.

"I am not ill. I know exactly what I am saying. Didn't your father tell you he agreed to us getting married?"

Married?! To Owen Pierce?! That had to be some kind of joke. Did he want her money? No, that couldn't be it. Her father was already helping with that. Was he being forced? Yes, that had to be it. The thoughts in her head ran wild.

"Veronica, are you all right?" He was worried. She wasn't saying anything or moving at all.

"Who is forcing you?" she said almost in a whisper. Owen was stunned. How did she know? He stood there, not saying anything, and that told her she was right. Tears welled in her eyes.

She took off around him and went running down the hall.

"Veronica!" Owen hollered after he came to his senses.

Railbert seeing what happened, hurriedly left. Henry and Ellen came out a few seconds later, finding Owen staring down the hall.

"What happened?" Henry asked.

"I thought you had already talked to her. I am so sorry," he said, looking down at the floor.

"Which way did she go?" Ellen asked. Owen pointed down the hall in the direction she had gone. Ellen started walking in that direction, knowing where Veronica would go.

"No, Veronica had just gotten back. We did not have a chance to talk to her but do not worry. Ellen will be able to calm her down.

Come, let us have a drink," said Henry as he grabbed Owen's shoulders, directing him toward the sitting room.

Ellen found Veronica sitting on a bench in the garden, staring off as tears rolled down her face. She walked up and sat beside her, not saying a word.

"Someone is forcing him, Mother."

"Why do you say that?"

"Why else would Owen Pierce marry me?" she said as more tears fell from her eyes.

"Ronnie, I do not know why he decided to marry you, but the only way you will find out is if you dry those tears and go be around him."

"What about Ada? Everyone said it was a done deal between them."

"That is what I am saying. You have questions, and only Owen can answer them. So, let us go and enjoy a pleasant supper, and tonight you can think about all the things you need to ask. Remember, you always need to think things through before you react and make a decision. You are more mature than you are acting right now." Ellen stood up and waited for an answer.

Veronica wiped her tears, stood up, and took a deep breath to calm herself down. "You are right. I am ready."

"That is my girl. Now, you must apologize for running away and be a considerate host tonight. Can you do that?" Ellen asked as she pushed curls away from Veronica's face.

"Yes, I can do that," she replied with a weak smile.

As they walked into the sitting room, Owen stood, looking very uncomfortable. She walked up to him, smiling.

"I am sorry for running off like that."

"It is perfectly understandable," he said with a smile.

"Let us go eat," said Henry, making his way to the door and smiling at his wife. She smiled back with a welcome look on her face.

The rest of the evening was calm and enjoyable. They talked about daily affairs, laughing at some of the antics Owen's friends had done, and for most of the evening, Veronica was a pleasant host. Owen studied her throughout the night and could tell her smile did not reach her eyes. He appreciated her trying to make the evening less awkward than it had started.

Before Owen left, he asked again if she would like to ride in the park tomorrow. She agreed with a smile. However, once he left, her smile disappeared.

"Come in here, Ronnie," her father said behind her. She walked into the sitting room where she saw Ellen on the couch, so she walked over and sat beside her.

"I know this came as a surprise, and the final decision will be yours. I only ask you to give it a chance?" said Henry as he sat in a chair across from her.

"I know, Father. It is just…" She looked down, not knowing how to word what she wanted to say.

"You do not think you are worthy of him?" Ellen said.

Veronica looked up at her, then back down, nodding.

"I do not know what to say to make you understand what a treasure you are," Henry said as he pinched the bridge of his nose. "I know me being your father, you think I say things to make you feel better, but I have never lied to you. I know Owen can grow to have feelings for you. So please, give it a chance." Henry fell quiet, waiting for a response.

Veronica thought for a few seconds, then looked at her dad. "I will give it an honest try," she replied, and everyone smiled.

"Good," said Henry as he stood along with both women.

"Today has been very trying. Let's get some rest tonight. Tomorrow starts something you have not had to do," says Ellen as they exit the room.

"What is that?" Veronica asked.

"Being courted. Now, go on to bed."

"All right. Goodnight."

Ellen and Henry watched as she disappeared up the stairs.

"You are worried about her?" Henry asked.

"You are not?"

"Yes, but all we can do is try to guide her and pray I made the right choice," says Henry as he puts his arm around her waist. They walk off toward their room.

The next day, Owen took Veronica horseback riding in the park, and as she feared, people stopped and stared. Some spoke, but most just whispered. She hated the attention but did enjoy talking to Owen. They seemed to have quite a bit in common.

He was surprised at how much she enjoyed riding, shooting, and even archery. Owen had thought Veronica soft and delicate like all the other women he knew, but she was far from it. It was rare to find a woman who had a sense of humor and was quick-witted. She seemed to have several different sides, and he was intrigued to see them all.

Making it back home, they immediately saw Henry walking toward them with a grim look.

"Father, what is wrong?"

"We need to leave for Blackthorn. There seem to be a few scoundrels going around terrorizing and robbing the tenants."

"When do we leave?"

"As soon as I get things squared away. Hopefully, tomorrow morning."

"Do you mind if I come along? It sounds dangerous, and I would like to help," Owen asked.

"If it is not too much of a bother. I have quite a few men but knowing you would be with Ronnie while she is helping the tenants would ease my mind. No matter what I say about the danger, which will be the first thing she does." Henry pulled her in for a hug.

"Then I will be leaving now so I can get things in order. I will be here in the morning. Lady Veronica," he said as he slightly bowed to her, turned, and walked out.

"Wait," Veronica hollered as she followed him out. He stopped and turned. "I had a lovely time. Thank you." She lowered her head and blushed.

"So did I." He smiled, then turned and walked away.

Veronica turned and almost ran into her father. He was standing there, watching with a big smile on his face. She rolled her eyes and walked past him, going to her room to start packing.

As she entered her room, she saw Lydia already filling her trunk.

"You are a blessing," she says as she gives Lydia a hug.

"I am almost done. How was the park?"

"Just like I thought it would be. People were staring and whispering." She plopped down on the coach. "How am I supposed to marry him? I cannot think when I am around him. All I want to do is stare at his handsome face. I will spend the rest of my life without a thought in my head."

Lydia softly giggled. "He is handsome."

"OH, Lydia, I forgot. I am the worse friend ever."

Lydia walked over and sat beside her.

"Veronica, you are a great friend, and that was a long time ago. I am happy now. Besides, there might be someone else," she said, blushing.

"Who? You have to tell me," Veronica said excitedly.

"Maybe Adrian." Lydia looked down, blushing more.

"That is wonderful. He is a good man. Have you told him who you are?"

"Yes, we have been honest with each other. I know who he is also. You are an amazing person. You should go for Owen, even if it leaves you cracked."

They both laughed and got up to finish packing.

"You need to go and stay at my Broad Street home while I am gone. Give you and Adrian a few weeks to relax and become closer." She smiled and nudged Lydia.

"Maybe I will."

Ellen walked by Veronica's room and stopped to listen to their laughter. She smiled, so glad to hear her happiness. *Maybe Owen will be a good thing* she thought as she continued to walk on past.

Her smile faded because she couldn't get passed the feeling that something was wrong.

When Owen returned home, he decided to inform his father of his intent to marry Veronica. He hesitated when he arrived at Callum's office door. Closing his eyes, he took a deep breath and knocked.

"Come in."

Owen opened the door and saw his father behind his desk going through papers. He looked tired and seemed to have aged.

"Oh, Owen, come in. I haven't seen you in a couple of days," Callum said as he put his pen down and sat back.

Owen walked in and sat in a chair facing the desk. "You look tired. Are you getting enough rest?"

"I will rest when our family is safe."

"Well, that might be sooner than you think." Seeing his dad like that made him more determined to marry.

"What do you mean?"

"I have not said anything because I was waiting to get Henry's approval and see how things were going to be with Veronica."

Callum sat forward with a confused look on his face.

"I am planning to marry Veronica." He held his breath, waiting to see how he would react.

"What? What about Ada? Did something happen?" Callum was utterly stunned.

"Ada and I have ended things."

"Let me guess. You told Ada about our troubles, and Agnes put a halt to your intentions."

"Yes, that is exactly what happened." Owen looked down, unable to look his father in the eye.

"Look, Owen, I know you might think the best way to recoup our losses is to marry Veronica, but I do not want you to enter a marriage you will be miserable in later. Agnes will rescind her disapproval once we get some income coming back in, and I do not want to see Henry's daughter in a loveless marriage, either."

"So, you disapprove?" Owen asked, surprised.

"I would like nothing more than to see you marry Veronica. She is everything a man could want in a wife. Not to mention Henry, as a father-in-law, the opportunity is limitless. So, what does Veronica say?"

"She was very receptive at first, but we went riding today, and I have to admit, she surprised me. Veronica is nothing like I thought she would be. Honestly, being married to her would not be so bad."

Callum was very quiet as he thought about the situation. "Well, if you are sure you could be happy with her, then I also give my approval," he said with a smile. He let out a deep breath and seemed to have relaxed visibly.

"I need to take care of some things and get packed. I am leaving in the morning. Henry is having some trouble at their country estate near Edinburgh," Owen said as he stood to leave.

"Son, be careful. Scots do not respond kindly to Englishmen. They tolerated Henry because he married Leah. So, watch your back."

"I will. You get some rest."

Owen then left and went to his bedroom, where he wrote a letter to his manager to handle his affairs while he was gone. As he was packing, he heard someone knocking.

"Come in."

"Owen," his mother said as she entered.

"Yes, Mother. What do you want?" He kept packing, never looking up.

"I was wondering how you were doing." She noticed him packing. "You are going somewhere?"

"Yes, I will be with Henry for a few days." He continued packing, still avoiding her gaze.

Ann walked up to him and put her hand on his shoulder. He visibly tensed. "Do you hate me?"

"No, but if you do not mind, I have much left to do before I go to bed."

She turned and left, wondering if he would ever forgive her.

# CHAPTER NINE

In order to be irreplaceable,
one must always be different

Coco Chanel

Owen arrived as the servants were loading everyone's trunks on the carriage. He noticed four men preparing horses for the journey as he handed his valise to load. They didn't look like ordinary servants. Their appearance and mannerism told him they must be ex-soldiers. He turned and walked to the open door, hearing Henry give Railbert instructions on things to do while he was gone.

"Oh, good morning, Owen. Right on time. We were going to eat a quick breakfast before we left. Would you like to join us?"

"Yes, I think I would."

They walked to the dining room where Veronica and Ellen were already eating. After sitting, they started discussing the trip.

"We will have to spend two nights at an inn. I have already sent a man ahead to secure our rooms." Henry turned to look at Veronica and stopped eating. "Veronica, you will ride in the carriage all the way this time. I want you with Ellen in case something happens. I do not foresee any danger, but I want to go on caution."

"Yes, Father."

Henry looked at her and squinted his eyes. "What, no argument?"

"Not today," she said, looking at her father with a massive smile on her face.

"Okay, now I am apprehensive. For you not to argue to ride that easy means you are probably going to do something I am not going to like."

"ME? Never," she replied, then looked at her plate and continued eating.

Ellen looked at Veronica, smiled, and shook her head, then continued eating.

Owen watched their interaction. You could feel the love they had for each other. He missed having that feeling with his family. Since this horrible plan started, he had not wanted to be around his mother. Owen wondered if he would ever have that again.

"Owen, I thought we would switch out riding with the ladies. But, in case there is trouble, someone needs to be with them."

"Sounds good."

"Is everybody done?" Henry asked as he stood.

"Yes," replied the woman.

"Good, let's get going."

After they were on their way, Owen decided to ask about the men accompanying them.

"Who are the men riding with us?"

"They are mine and Veronica's private guards," replied Ellen.

"Private guards? Are they ex-soldiers?"

"Yes, sort of. They were soldiers with unique skills. They even worked for the crown for a while," said Veronica.

*Spies, dangerous men indeed, but good in a fight,* thought Owen.

As the journey progressed, Owen was riding behind the carriage when he noticed one of the men riding up beside him.

"So, you want to marry Lady Veronica?" he asked, not looking at him.

"Yes, I do." As Owen spoke, he noticed another rider had come up on the other side. He then looked back to see the other two right behind him. They had him boxed in with the carriage in front of him.

"We think very highly of Lady Veronica. We have vowed to protect her from any danger. No matter who it is," said the first man as he turned to give Owen a scathing look.

"Glad to hear it," said Owen with more confidence than he felt, knowing that was a clear warning.

"I'm Aaron." He held out his hand.

"Owen," he replied as he reached out and shook his hand. Then the rest of the men started introducing themselves.

"William."

"Ian."

"Michael."

Their attitude seems to have completely changed as they talked to Owen. In no time, they seemed to have become friends.

After a while, the carriage stopped, and everyone exited, stretching and walking around. Owen dismounted and walked to Henry, watching Veronica as she walked to one of the guards and started rubbing the horse's face and neck.

"Why are you not riding this time?" asked Ian.

"Father thought I would be safe in the carriage."

All four men chuckled.

"I feel sorry for anyone who tangles with you," said William.

Owen heard the conversation and wondered what they meant. He shrugged it off as playful banter.

"We are almost there. I am going to ride with you the rest of the way. The carriage gets too cramped for me," said Henry as he untied his horse.

"Ready to continue, ladies? We don't have much further."

A couple of hours later, they came around a bend in the road, and there were no more trees, only open land for miles. Owen stopped his horse as he stared at a massive square fortress with two circular towers on each end.

"It's a castle," Owen stated with a shocked expression.

"Yes, castle Blackthorn. Old Tyrin Brannon was a very wealthy Scotsman. Unfortunately, his son died in a war, so he left everything to Leah. He was a mean son of a bitch, but he loved his daughter and doted on his grandchildren."

"What was Veronica's mother like?"

Henry stopped and looked to his left at the hill in the distance. Owen followed his gaze and saw a structure with a fence around it.

"She is buried up there. Leah loved her home so much, I thought it was only right to bring her here." He paused as he stared in the direction of her grave. "She was an incredible woman. Not a mean bone in her body. She never overlooked anybody who needed help and had a brilliant mind for finances. Veronica is so much like her."

"Really?"

"Yes, Veronica manages two orphanages and a house on Broad's Street. I know it is unusual for women to be in control of so much, but I want her to be capable. I have also given her some of the responsibility here, and she is doing excellently. Soon, I will hand it entirely over to her."

"This is Veronica's?"

"Yes, Ellis preferred another estate further east, so this one goes to Veronica. It will not be in the marriage contract. Right now, it is in

Ellis's name, which will remain until Veronica has children. It has to stay with direct descendants."

Owen was in complete awe. He'd never imagined Veronica was that wealthy.

Crossing the drawbridge, he looked at the wide mote and massive walls. There was no way one could attack that place and win. Once inside, there was a vast courtyard. To the right was a beautiful garden with several walkways, and he got a glimpse of a fountain. Looking left, he saw horse stalls. Enough for at least twenty horses. He couldn't wait to see the inside.

Outside the main doors, standing on the stairs, a line of servants waited with big smiles on their faces. Veronica jumped out as soon as the carriage stopped and hugged the servants.

A man walked out the doorway, and Owen wondered if he was seeing things.

"That man looks like—"

"Railbert," Said Henry, as he knew what Owen was going to say. "He is Railbert's twin brother, Ailbert. Their names might sound the same and look alike, but you won't find two people more different."

After Veronica finished her hug, she turned to Ailbert, ran toward him, and leaped into his arms. He picked her up and hugged her tightly.

"How's my little lassie?" he said with a big smile.

Henry, Ellen, and Owen walked up the stairs, and Ailbert set Veronica down.

"My Lord, my Lady," he says as he slightly bows. "Rooms are ready and food prepared for after you have freshened up."

"Thank you," said Ellen.

"Ailbert, this is Lord Pierce. He has come to help and accompany Veronica while she is out on the grounds," said Henry.

"Welcome, my Lord." He bows slightly to Owen.

"Thank you." Owen studies Ailbert, noticing several differences between him and his brother. Mainly the lack of grey around his temples and the wide grin on his face. He can't remember Railbert ever smiling.

After going to their rooms and changing clothes, they all met in the dining room. Owen couldn't help but look around the vast space that could easily hold at least a couple hundred people.

While eating, they discussed how to start their search for the robbers.

"I have men coming in the morning to assist Veronica. I know you want to see the tenants, so you will take the guards along with Owen," said Henry.

"Do you not need them with you?"

"No, I want them to go with you. I will have plenty with me. It will be less worrisome if they are with you."

"All right," she replied.

"You have become so agreeable lately," he said, smiling.

"Yes, I have," Veronica said, smiling back at her father.

"Okay, it is late, and we need to rise early in the morning." Ellen stood. She was so glad Veronica didn't argue with her father. He worried so much about her.

Owen followed Veronica out. She noticed him looking at the tapestries along the way.

"Would you like a tour tomorrow before we head out?"

"Yes, I would like that very much."

"Okay, after breakfast, then." She explained some of the tapestries on the wall as they made their way up the stairs.

"Have a good night," said Owen as Veronica stopped in front of her room.

"You as well." After she entered her room, she laid back against the door, thinking about the last two days. She and Owen seemed to be more relaxed around each other. She smiled, thinking maybe she could be happy with him.

The following day, Owen entered the dining room, seeing Henry at the head of the table with Ellen on his left. At the other end, William, Ian, Aaron, and Michael sat eating.

"Veronica has not made it for breakfast?" Owen asked as he sat two seats down from Henry.

"Not yet. She will be down any minute," said Ellen.

Not long after, Veronica walked in, and everyone stopped eating and looked at her. The four guards continue eating as if nothing were strange, while Henry, Ellen, and Owen were shocked at how she was dressed in breeches and a man's shirt, tucked in.

"What are you wearing? I told you I do not want you dressing as a man anymore," said Henry in a raised voice.

After Veronica filled her plate, she sat between Owen and her father.

"Father, you know I am going to be riding today. Would you rather I straddle my horse in a gown pulled up to my knees?" she asked, her head turned sideways, looking at him.

Owen choked on his food and started coughing. He took a drink of his water to try and stop. He tried to hide his smile as he thought how much he would like to see that.

"I let you come up here way too much when you were young," said Henry, shaking his head.

"Do not worry. I will have enough protection with me today," She replied and started eating.

After everyone finished eating, Veronica told her guards they would leave a little later after giving Owen a tour. Their first stop was the library. Owen stood in the middle and looked up. It was at least two floors high with a ladder that went all the way around. He had not seen such an enormous number of books since attending Oxford. He especially noticed the handmade furniture.

"Can I ask a question?" Owen asked as he ran his hand over a desktop.

"Why the rough-looking furniture?"

"Yes."

"A man in town makes furniture, so I commission all I needed from him."

"He does good work. Is this mahogany?"

"Yes. Ellis brought a ship full of it and gave me enough to make this library."

After they left the library, they entered a long hall full of paintings.

"This is the ancestral hall," said Veronica.

Owen looked at each picture, intrigued. Veronica walked ahead and stopped at the end of the hall, looking up at one of the pictures. Owen walked up beside her.

"These are my grandparents."

Owen looked and saw a woman with long red hair and big brown eyes sitting in a high-back chair. Next to her was a tall, large man with black hair and grey eyes, wearing a kilt. He had a stern, cold look on his face, while the woman had a big, warm smile.

"Her name was Ceana. I never met her, but she looks kind."

"Yes, not like him."

"Grampa could be grumpy, but I have only beautiful memories. Ellis and I would come and spend the summers with him, and even though he hated England, he would come every Christmas and stay past New Year's. I loved him very much," she said as tears threatened to spill from her eyes.

He looked at her and could see the love in her eyes.

"Come, I want to show you my special place."

Owen kelp glancing at Veronica's backside as they walked up the stairs. Her hair was in a single braid which left her bottom exposed. Her pants fit snugly and showed off her curvy rear end. He couldn't help but think what it would feel like to have his hands on it.

They finally stopped climbing stairs and walked into a small empty room. Owen noticed it was one of the round towers.

"I would come up here to be alone. I did some of my best thinking up here," Veronica said as she walked to the open window. Owen walked up beside her and was amazed at the view. He could see for miles. Just green fields and rolling hills in the distance.

"Beautiful."

"Yes, it is."

"Are you going to change this room?"

"No, I like to leave this room untouched. There's one more room I would like to show you."

They left the tower and walked to the other side of the castle, where they came upon two massive doors.

"Help me push them open?" Veronica asked as she put her body up against the door.

Owen was surprised as they walked into a vast room with a long table in the center. Two massive fireplaces were at each end of the room. At the end of the hall were steps that led up to a stage, where a single chair sat. It looked like a place a leader or a king would sit.

"I thought the room we had breakfast in was big," said Owen as he walked around.

"This room is called Shield Hall. This is where clans would gather for different reasons."

"Like what?"

"Celebrations, at times to discuss war tactics, but mostly to solve problems between clans. They would hang their tartan and shield along the wall. The clan colors said they had a representative here, and their shield told them they were here to talk, not fight."

"Amazing," said Owen as he continued around the room. He stopped when he realized Veronica wasn't with him. He looked back and saw she was still near the stage, looking at the floor, lost in thought.

He walked back to her side. "Veronica, is something wrong?"

"No. Sorry, I was woolgathering. Ready to head out to see the tenants with me?"

"Yes, let's go."

Walking out the main doors, they saw Veronica's guards had readied the horses and were waiting. Owen was impressed by Veronica's horsemanship as they rode out across the open fields. She rode better than most men. He couldn't help but smile as he thought about her comment that morning, referring to her gown riding up to her knees. She definitely had a free spirit.

The first tenant's home they came to seemed like nobody was home. Well maintained and quite large for a tenant's home. Veronica dismounted and knocked on the door.

After a few seconds, an elderly man opened the door, surprised Veronica was standing there. "Miss Veronica," he said, extremely nervous.

"Mr. McCauley, how are you?"

"Good. What brings ye here?" He looked behind her, saw the men, and looked around as if he was looking for someone else.

"I am here to check on things. We heard about the trouble with the tenants and the robberies. Have you had any incidents?"

"No, no, I have not," he answered quickly.

Veronica could tell something was wrong. "Are Kieran and Sienaid home? I would like to see them."

"No, gone to town."

She decided to act like she didn't notice he was behaving strangely. "All right, tell them, I said hello. We will be going now."

Once they were on their way, Veronica stopped, and everyone followed suit.

"What is wrong?" asked Owen.

"Something was wrong back at the McCauley's. He has always been happy to see me. I just have a terrible feeling. Come on, let us go to Mccloud's."

They soon arrived and received the same reaction.

"Mr. McCloud, is Sean home?"

"No."

"Oh, all right. Can I speak to Mrs. McCloud? I want to go over some ideas I have for her garden."

"No, she has gone to town. I have things to do. I will tell em when they get back." He quickly shut the door.

She walked back to where everyone had dismounted.

"All right, I see what you mean. He acted the same way the other guy did," said Owen.

"Yes, and everyone has conveniently gone to town. The problem is, his wife never goes to town." Veronica turned and walked to her horse. "I wonder how long it is going to take to find those highwaymen."

As soon as Veronica finished speaking, they heard horses galloping and looked to see four men in hoods riding toward them.

"That did not take long," said Aaron. He nodded to the other three as if giving a silent command.

The four men separated to provide enough distance so the robbers would have a hard time watching all of them. They knew that once they saw Veronica, their attention would be on her.

Owen grabbed Veronica and pushed her behind him. She stood looking at his back, completely stunned, and her heart warmed that he was trying to protect her.

The four men come to a quick halt in front of them. Two had pistols drawn and pointing at each one of them as a warning. The man in the front dismounted, and the two unarmed men followed. The last stayed mounted, still pointing his pistol.

"Well, what do we have here? It is just our luck we came across you fine gents. We will be taking any money you have and your horses." They could tell immediately that he was English.

Everyone remained silent, not even making a slight movement.

"But first, we have gotten wind the Aldridges have returned. I would be lenient on what we take if someone could tell us where the daughter is. We know she visits all the tenants when she is here."

Everyone remained silent. Veronica leaned and looked around Owen and waved at the guy.

"I am here. How can I help you?" Veronica says as she steps around him.

"What are you doing?" he asked as he grabbed her arm.

"Trust me, I will be okay." She looked Owen in the eyes and smiled, trying to reassure him, but he wouldn't let her go. She put her hand on top of his. "I will be all right," she said again.

Owen looked towards Aaron for help and saw him nod, telling him it was okay. He reluctantly let go of her arm. She walked up to the man and stood about two feet away from him.

"You are Veronica Aldridge?" He looked her up and down, taking in how she was dressed. The corner of his mouth raised slightly as an evil glint could be seen in his eyes.

"Yes, I am." Before anyone knew what was happening, Veronica lunged at the man and had him disarmed and on his knees in a chokehold.

At the same time, Ian hollered and spooked the horse with the rider still on. The horse reared up, causing the rider to discharge his pistol into the air as he tumbled off. In seconds, he had the man subdued. The other two men went to their knees and pulled off their hoods.

Once Veronica was sure the man she was choking was out cold, she let go of him. Standing and turning to check on the other two, she stopped dead in her tracks.

"Sean, Kieran? What are you doing with these people?"

"Miss Veronica, we didn't have a choice. They came and took Sienaid and Sean's mom. If we didn't do what they said, they would kill them," said Kieran as he lowered his head in shame.

"You know these two?" asked Owen.

"Yes, they are the ones supposed to be in town."

"We need to notify the magistrate and figure this out," said Aaron as he tied up the unconscious man.

"No, you cannot. He is the man behind it," said Sean.

"Magistrate Conners?" asked Veronica.

"No, he is no longer magistrate. Dougal is."

"What! How in the blazes did Dougal become a magistrate? He is such a coward and not someone you can trust."

"You have been gone a long time. A lot has changed," said Kieran.

"Okay, let us return to the castle before someone sees us. There we can get to the bottom of this," she says as she walks over to Sean and Kieran.

"I promise we will get them back."

They both stood and hugged her.

During the ride back, Owen got up beside Veronica. "How well do you know those two?"

"We would play together when I came for the summer. That was until my season started three years ago. I have not been here since. I should have skipped some of that and come back."

He could hear the self-blame in her voice.

"This is not your fault. Things happen, and people make choices you cannot control. Sometimes they are forced to do things they never thought they were capable of." Owen looked off as he realized he was also talking about himself. "Where did you learn to fight like that? You had him on the ground in no time."

"Ellis started teaching me to fight when I was young. Mainly boxing and some things that would make a man let go of me. He was worried about when it was time for me to enter society. So, whenever he came home from school, he would take the time to teach me and make sure I was practicing. Then Father hired these four guards, and they have been teaching me what you saw today."

"You are truly incredible," said Owen as he stared at Veronica. He always thought women were weak and needed constant protection. Not Veronica. He thought of his sister and how he should teach her how to protect herself.

Once they made it back to the castle, she had Ailbert prepare two rooms for Sean and Kieran while they placed the two men tied up in one of the towers.

Ailbert returned not long after they were finished.

"Rooms are ready, miss."

"Ian, William, do you have any clothes these two can borrow?"

"Yes, we can get them something," said Ian, then they walked towards the stairs.

Veronica turned to Sean and Kieran. "You two follow Ailbert to your rooms. There should be bathwater prepared already. Once you are clean, there will be food prepared."

The two looked down, embarrassed.

"They didn't let us take care of ourselves," said Sean.

"It is okay. We are going to make things right."

"Thank you," said Sean.

"So glad you are back," said Kieran.

She watched as they disappeared up the stairs, then immediately turned toward Michael and Aaron. "Michael, I need you to go to Dalkeith. Tell Magistrate Gregor we need him at Blackthorn Castle. He was a friend of my grandfather and had a good relationship with my father. Talk to no one else but him.

"Aaron, I need you to track my father and tell him what happened, not any of the men. We don't know whom we can trust. Go, hurry."

"Yes, miss," they both said at the same time and hurriedly left.

Owen watched as Veronica gave orders without hesitation. She was confident and made decisions quickly, making his respect for her grow even more. He sometimes forgot his true purpose as he spent more time with her, but then it came back, and so did the sick feeling.

"I need to get cleaned up myself," said Owen as he walked towards the stairs but stopped and turned back around.

"I know I have said this already, but you truly are amazing." He then continued up the stairs.

Veronica smiled and watched Owen as he walked away. Should she accept his proposal? It had been so hectic the last couple of days that she hadn't had time to think about it. She headed to her room to change before her father returned, knowing he would be upset with her still dressed as a man.

An hour later, everyone was in the great hall eating. Sean and Kieran were devouring the food. Looking up, Sean saw Ellen watching them.

"Sorry for our lack of manners. We have not eaten in the last few days."

"You do not need to apologize. I need you two to eat as much as possible. You will need your strength," said Veronica.

Sean looked at Veronica and smiled. Nobody noticed the pain and longing in his eyes.

"I am sorry this has happened to your families. Once Henry is back, we will do everything we can to put right this wrong," said Ellen.

"Thank you, my Lady," said Kieran.

Right after they finished eating, Henry and his men returned. Sean and Kieran explained everything that had happened.

"Do you have any idea where they are being held?" asked Henry.

"Lord Donaldson has them."

Henry and Veronica looked at each other with worried expressions.

"Do you know him?" asked Owen.

"Yes, afraid so. Lord Donaldson and old man Brannon had an ugly relationship," said Henry.

"They hated each other," corrected Veronica.

"Old Lord Donaldson is dead. He died a year ago. His son Liam is the Lord now," spoke Kieran.

"The old lord got in good with magistrate Dougal. Not sure what happened, but that's how he got Lord Liam to do what he wanted," Sean said.

"So, Lord Donaldson is also being coerced? We can use this," said Veronica.

"That is enough for tonight. We wait for Magistrate Gregor before we make a plan. Make sure this is done legally so Dougal gets the punishment he deserves." Henry stood, causing everyone to stand and leave the room.

"Sean, Kieran, you both need to get a good night's sleep. You have had to bare this burden too long, so I need you rested and with a clear mind. Because tomorrow we make plans to end this," said Veronica.

Both Sean and Kieran walked up and hugged Veronica.

While Kieran hugged her, he whispered, "Donaldson likes Seinaid." He then let go and went to his room.

Veronica thinks about what Kieran told her. *If he has feelings for her, then we can use that.*

"Veronica, wait. I need to speak to you," said Henry.

"Yes, Father?"

"I know you will want to be in the middle of this tomorrow, but I need you to stay out of this. I do not mind you being in the meetings, but that is it."

Veronica stood there for a few seconds. "Okay," she said, then turned and left.

"Why do I not believe her?" Henry looked at Ellen.

Ellen just shook her head. "You can never tell what that girl will do."

Veronica went to her room. She was going to tell her father about Lord Donaldson and Sienaid but decided not to since she was excluded from the plan. It upset her that she could sit in the meeting, but nothing else.

*So, I will make my own plan,* she thought with a smile.

# CHAPTER TEN

The best protection
A woman can have
is courage

Elizabeth Stanton

Magistrate Gregor arrived the next morning and was filled in on everything.

"I cannot believe this has been happening. We need to either get him to admit what he has done or find proof," said Gregor.

"We need to talk to Lord Donaldson without Dougal finding out. When do you take your bounty, and where?" asked Veronica.

"After a couple of robberies, if they are big enough, we take it to Lord Donaldson," replied Sean.

"Has it been a while since your last delivery?"

"Aye."

"Good. We will go in disguise as the robbers."

"You are not going," said Owen and Henry at the same time.

"Okay, if you two do not want me going, I will stay here."

Henry stared at Veronica with an uncertain look on his face. She turned and walked to the door. "I will let you men hash out the details of your plan." She then exited the room.

"That was way too easy," said Henry, looking at Owen.

"Huh." Owen looked confused.

"You have not learned her yet. She agreed too easily."

Sean and Kieran looked at each other and smiled. They knew Veronica was not the type just to agree and walk away. She definitely had something planned.

They were right. She did have something planned and had to hurry if she was going to get it accomplished.

First, she had to dress accordingly. Wanting to give a familiar look, not a wealthy Aldridge one, she donned a simple beige gown. Next, she wrapped her braided hair into a tight bun. She knew she had to play her Scottish heritage if Lord Donaldson were to give her an audience. Then, using her grandfather's colors, she wrapped a Brannon clan shawl around her shoulders. It was risky with the history between the two clans, but she had a better chance than using her English heritage.

Once she was ready, she and her maid, Beatrice, made their way out of the castle through hidden hallways only Ellis and a few servants knew. A carriage with a blackthorn crest was waiting, and they were out of the courtyard before the men. Veronica knew the carriage would take longer, and the men might catch up, but it would catch less attention. She just hoped luck was on her side.

If Kieran was correct and Lord Donaldson had feelings for Seinaid, she might be able to get him to join them.

Henry, Owen, Kieran, Sean, and the four guards left a little while after Veronica. Once they got there, the guards would hide in the trees while the rest went to the estate and waited until nightfall to make a move.

As the large estate came into view through the tree line, they saw a carriage pull up to the steps.

"Bloody hell," said Henry.

"What is wrong?" asked Owen.

"That is Veronica that just stepped out of that carriage. I knew she agreed too easily. One day, she is going to get herself killed."

Owen was shocked. Was it bravery or stupidity that led her to jump straight into danger? Once married, he would put a stop to her carelessness.

It didn't take but a second to remember he wouldn't be married to her long enough for her to even care about what he thought. Sadness crept into his heart, which surprised him.

"We always go around to the stables. There will be men that will take the goods. You do not have to worry about them looking at you. It is like they were ordered not to," said Sean.

"What about Veronica?" asked Owen.

"I know she has a plan. Let us just hope it works. We will be inside, so if she needs help, we will have a better chance to get to her," replied Henry.

Veronica walked up and used the large knocker on the door. It opened, and an elderly butler stood there, somewhat surprised. "Lady Aldridge, how can I help you?"

"You know me?" Veronica was shocked.

"I knew your mother. It was not hard to recognize you," he said with a smile and a thick Scottish accent.

He stepped back and allowed Veronica and Beatrice to enter.

"I am here to see Lord Donaldson."

"Please, wait while I tell my lord." He walked down the hall and entered a room on the left.

"Who is here?" she heard a man's voice yell from the room.

A few seconds later, a man little over six feet, wearing a kilt, walked out. He was well built, like most Scotsman, with brown wavy hair and blue eyes. Not bad looking but nowhere as handsome as Owen. He seemed to be in his thirties, a lot younger than she'd imagined.

She couldn't help but wonder how Owen would look in a kilt.

"Never would I have believed Tyrin Brannon's granddaughter would set foot in Donaldson estate. What do I owe this visit to?" he said with a smile.

"I need your help. Can we speak privately?" Veronica replied, smiling back.

"Of course. This way," he said as he walked back into the room and waited until Veronica and Beatrice entered before shutting the door. The room must have been his office, for there was a desk to the right. To the left was a small couch and two chairs across from it. The furniture looked worn.

*So, financial trouble,* she thought.

"Please sit."

Veronica and Beatrice walked over and sat on the couch, and Liam sat across from them. "I am here to ask for your help to bring Dougal to justice." Liam's face grew pale, and he sat back.

"What do you know?"

"I know you have the captives here. I know you are being forced into helping him because of something your father did."

"I cannot help you," he said as he got up.

"Look, I can help you," she said, also standing.

"No, you cannot. I refused to help Dougal at first, but he already had enough evidence to make me hang. The things my father got involved in, Dougal kept the evidence and made it look like it was me. I can either pay five thousand pounds or do as he says.

"I do not have the money to get out. My father left this place almost destitute. So you see you cannot help me." He walked over to the window and stared out as if lost.

"The money is yours."

He spins around, completely taken back. "Why would you do that? Why help me?"

"I am not doing this just for you. I am doing this for my friends and tenants. I am doing this to stop a man like Dougal, hoping this will end the feud between our clans. Whatever it was that caused it."

There was silence between them as they stared at each other.

"It was your grandmother," said Liam.

"Pardon?"

"My father and your grandfather both courted your grandmother. Of course, she chose Brannon, which devastated my father. He became bitter and cold."

"I had no idea." *So, love can destroy,* she thought.

"Let me hear this plan of yours," he said as he walked back and sat down.

As they sat there and talked, Liam started to admire Veronica.

"It was very brave of you to come here alone."

"I did not come alone. I have Beatrice, and I must tell you we have already captured the men and replaced them with our own. I knew you would be a reasonable man and help us. I just had to prove it to my father. He is probably mad at me because I did not tell him I was coming here."

Liam chuckled. "I imagine he stays mad at you."

"Yes, he does." She smiled and lowered her head.

"If this works, I will be indebted to you."

"No, I hope you know you can rely on your neighbor in hard times," said Veronica with all honesty.

"I believe you." Liam smiled. For the first time in months, he had hope.

Someone knocked.

"Come in."

"My Lord, Kieran is here," said the butler.

Veronica watched Liam's face drop, and a sad look entered his eyes. So, it must have been true about his feelings for Seinaid.

"Send him in."

The butler stepped back, and Kieran walked in. He took a look at Veronica and smiled.

'I knew you would not stay home like a good lass. Your father is rightly mad."

"Yes, I kind of thought he would be, but I knew he would not agree to my plan. I had to try and end this the best way possible without conflict. Dougal is our enemy, not Lord Donaldson."

"I agree with you, but you might want to let Lord Henry calm down first. May I see my sister, Lord Donaldson?"

"Yes, of course. I believe she is still in her room."

"They are in the estate?" Veronica said, surprised.

"Aye, you thought I put them in the dungeon?" he said, teasing.

Veronica blushed. "Well, actually, yes." She started laughing.

Liam couldn't help but find Veronica brilliant and charming. He had heard things about her but did not dare to believe them true. Thank God; she was exactly like he'd heard.

"Well, I guess I should face my father and tell him the plan Lord Donaldson and I have come up with."

"Please, just Liam," he said with a smile.

"Kieran, would you tell the rest of them to come inside before you see Seinaid?" asked Veronica.

"Aye, miss," said Kieran as he turned to leave the room.

"Before they get here, let me show you something." Liam walked to the bookshelf and shoved it aside, revealing a space big enough for two or three people to fit comfortably.

"Perfect," said Veronica.

Liam put the shelf back, and they walked back and sat down.

"Ready to face your father, Lady Aldridge?"

"Please, just Veronica," she said, smiling.

"And I might as well be." He took a deep breath, preparing for the confrontation. After a short while, they heard a knock.

"Come in."

"My Lord, you have visitors."

"Let them in."

As Henry walked in, his first look was at Veronica. He walked up to her and waited as she slowly raised her head to meet his angry eyes. "We will talk about this later."

She nodded her head, not saying anything.

"Lord Donaldson, thank you for seeing us. This is Lord Pierce."

"Pleasure to meet you," Liam said to Owen.

"Likewise," Owen replied.

"Let us get down to business. I am aware you know my part in this with Dougal. Veronica and I have come up with a plan to trap him into confessing, but we need Magistrate Gregor here as a witness."

"I want to hear this plan," said Henry.

"Gregor and Veronica will be hiding when Dougal comes to pick up the money. It will be enough that he will come personally to get it."

"How are you going to get him to confess?" asked Owen.

"He is arrogant and thinks nobody can touch him."

"Veronica will not be involved. I will be here instead," said Henry.

"No, it will not work with you, Father. If this goes to trial, the people here will not listen to an Englishman. We have to admit I am the best person. Everyone around this area knows the bad blood between our clans. If the granddaughter of Tyrin Brannon testifies for a Donaldson, who would not believe me?"

"Veronica speaks the truth. No offense, but the people will not pay a half pence to a Sassenach."

Owen got angry when he heard Liam call Veronica by her name. When did they become so intimate? He would not' admit to himself that he was jealous, instead he would just brush it off as inappropriate behavior he would have her correct.

Henry was quiet, thinking about the situation.

"I do not' like it," said Owen, not taking his eyes off Liam.

Veronica looked at Owen and noticed the glare he was giving Liam. "I will be safe, especially with Magistrate Gregor here."

"I insist on being here. I 'will not leave your safety in 'any other hands," said Owen, still not taking his eyes off Liam.

Liam realized that Owen had a thing for Veronica and thought he was a threat. It would be fun to play with that Sassenach. He walked around his desk and stands close to Veronica.

"I swear on everything I have left, I will not let anything happen to the bonnie lass."

Veronica turned to look at Liam and smiled, for she was relieved the feud was over between them. That, of course, Owen mistook for flirting and grew even angrier.

Before he could say anything, Henry spoke up. "I still would feel at ease if Lord Pierce was also here."

"Yes, of course," said Liam, pleased with the effect on Owen's face. It was hard for him not to laugh.

"Well, we will see you in two days time," said Veronica.

"Actually, you will need to come the night before. Once I send word, he will have someone to look around to make sure it is not a trap."

"How are you so sure Dougal will come himself?"

"He trusts nobody, especially with a large amount."

"Okay, we shall do that," said Veronica.

"Let us get going. We need to fill the magistrate in on our plan. Lord Liam," said Henry as he nodded and turned to leave.

Veronica held out her hand to Liam, and he kissed it, lingering just a little too long for Owen's comfort. She then turned and left with Beatrice and Owen in tow.

Liam smiled, knowing he got under that Englishmen's skin.

Once they returned to the castle, Veronica hurriedly left the carriage and tried to make it to her room.

"Stop right there," said Ellen.

"Mother, we have a wonderful plan, and Lord Liam is very agreeable. The feud between our clans is over. Did you know it was all about my grandmother?" she rambled on, trying to redirect the discussion she knew was coming.

"Veronica, stop talking," She said firmly. "Go into the study and wait for your father. I am sure he will want to talk to you since you left after he told you to stay out of it."

Veronica lowered her head and walked toward the study.

Ellen shook her head and smiled as she watched Veronica pout.

Henry and Owen walked in shortly after Veronica entered the study.

"Where is she?" Henry asked when he saw Ellen.

"In your study. Please, do not' be too harsh with her."

He said nothing as he walked to his study.

"Is everything going to be, okay?" asked Owen.

"Yes, he will never hurt her. He loves her so much. She has always been strong-willed. Always getting into things as a child. Henry would say it is the Scot's blood in her. We both worry about what could happen to her."

"I think Lord Donaldson is interested in her," said Owen, hoping she would put a stop to it before anything could get started.

"Really, huh?" Is all she said as she walked away. Owen seemed unsettled about Lord Donaldson. *Maybe Owen can come to care about her,* she thought.

Owen wondered if he should wait to make sure things didn't get out of hand. Henry was furious, and as he feared, he could hear him hollering. He walked to the door and started listening. He knew he shouldn't, but a part of him wanted to go and protect her. Knowing he had no right to interfere, all he could do was listen to Henry rant and rave. He heard not a word from Veronica. He pictured her sitting with her head down, acting obedient.

"Veronica, look at me," said Henry.

She looked up with a remorseful expression.

"You have no idea what it is like to have a child. To love that child so much, you live in fear of them getting hurt." He took a deep breath and let it out slowly. "Veronica, please stop being reckless."

"I am sorry, Father," she said in a whisper.

"You may go." He didn't look at her.

She got up and opened the door to find Owen waiting. She closed the door and walked toward him.

"Are you okay?" Owen asked.

They both turned and walked toward the stairs.

"I truly do not mean to make him worry. But I do have to admit that sometimes I do things without thinking about how he would feel."

"Yes, I have come to realize you are fearless. You do jump straight into situations," he said with a smile.

"Well, I guess you will change your mind about wanting to marry me because, even though I say I will change, I probably 'will not." She stopped in front of her room and turned to face him.

"On the contrary, you fascinate me."

He moved toward her and leaned down. He was so close, she could feel his breath on her face. She watched as his eyes moved down to her lips. She held her breath, not knowing what to do. He slowly moved towards her, giving her a chance to stop him, but she didn't.

When their lips touched, she froze, amazed at how warm they felt. The feeling of that warmth spread all over her body. She wrapped her arms around his neck as he pulled her close. His tongue licked her lips, causing her to gasp and allowing his tongue to thrust into her mouth. The feeling she was developing made her dizzy and her legs weak.

He finally pulled back and rested his forehead against hers as he caught his breath. He didn't know what came over him, but he liked it.

He finally steps back and looks at her flushed face. "See you at dinner?" as all he could think to say.

"Yes," she replied as she turned and entered her room.

Beatrice was laying out her evening attire inside when she saw Veronica walk in and shut the door, leaning against it. She had her hand on her chest as if she was having trouble breathing.

"What's wrong, miss?"

"Owen just kissed me," she said as if she didn't believe it.

"Is that not good?"

Veronica smiled. "Yes, I guess it is."

Later that evening, things seemed to have eased up with Henry at supper. The conversation was light, and everyone avoided the topic of the next day's' plans. Owen and Veronica occasionally make eye contact, where she quickly looked away, and he smiled, blushing. Ellen noticed their exchanges and wondered what was going on.

After finishing supper, everyone got up to leave.

"Veronica, stay for a minute, please," Said, Ellen.

"Gentlemen, would you care for a drink before we retire?" asked Henry.

"Most certainly," replied Magistrate Gregor.

"Yes, I believe I would," said Owen

"What would you like to talk about?" Asked Veronica after the men left.

"I noticed something different about you and Owen. Has something happened?"

Veronica lowered her head. "Owen kissed me."

"That is all? He just kissed you?"

"Yes, it was so amazing. I never dreamed it would feel like that," she said with a big smile on her face.

Ellen walked over to Veronica and looked at her. "Yes, a kiss can be wonderful. However, it can also cloud your judgment and allow you to do things you should not. Always remember what is appropriate. Do you understand?"

"Yes, Mother. I will."

Ellen wrapped her arms around her. Her little girl was growing up. She pulled back and moved a few strands of hair out of her face. "Your father told me of the plan. Promise me you will be safe."

"I will, I promise."

"Now, go to bed and get some rest. Hopefully, this will be over soon."

Veronica left the room, and Ellen stood there, thinking. Maybe it was a good sign, about the kiss. Yes, she would let it be a good sign.

# CHAPTER ELEVEN

Love could be labeled as poison,
but we'd drink it anyway

Atticus

Veronica asked Owen to meet her in the library after breakfast the following day. She had decided it was time to ask some questions. Owen entered the library and found her sitting by the window.

"Veronica?"

"Come in, take a seat."

He walked over and sat beside her. "Why did you want to see me?"

She looked up at him. "What happened with Ada?"

Owen wasn't surprised. He knew the questions would eventually happen. "Agnes decided she wanted someone else for her daughter."

"Someone not in financial trouble?" Veronica said, knowing that could be the only reason for Agnes to change her mind.

"You know?"

"Yes, Dinah told me. She was so upset and scared."

Owen had no idea how Dinah felt about the situation. He'd never talked to her about it. "I must be the worse brother ever. I never even talked to her about it." He put his face in his hands.

"No, you are not. You have a lot of pressure on you. I know you want to help your family; she loves you so much."

He took a deep breath, thinking about his sister. He loved her, too, and had to make sure she was safe and protected. The thought of her being scared bothered him tremendously.

"Is it my dowry that you want?"

"I will not deny that was a part of it, but Veronica, you are unbelievable. You are nothing like I thought you were."

"Better or worse?" She looked at him with squinted eyes, warning him about his answer.

He chuckled at her expression. "Better, trust me."

"So, since you couldn't have Ada, you settled for me?"

"NO! Do not even think that, Veronica. You are interesting, fun, and brilliant. You deserve so much more. More than me." He looks away, wanting so badly to tell the truth. He needed to tell her the truth, but he couldn't.

Veronica reached out and grabbed his hand. "I never knew the kind of person you were, only what Dinah said. Since you have been around, I can tell you are generous, brave, and protective. I noticed that when you shoved me behind you when those men came riding upon us."

"Well, we know how that ended. My chivalry was not needed."

"Oh, yes, it was. It showed me what kind of person you are. You actually made me feel protected. Thank you for that."

They stared into each other's eyes briefly before she looked away.

"Do you think you can grow to care about me? I am not asking for love but some sort of affection?" asked Veronica, not looking at him.

"I do believe I could grow to have affection for you." For some unknown reason, Owen did not feel it was a lie.

Veronica looked up at him and smiled.

"So, have you made a decision?"

"Yes, I have." She took a deep breath while he held his. "Yes, I will marry you."

He grabbed her and pulled her into a hug. "Thank you." As he hugged her, he smelled a light fragrance of jasmine. He was becoming attracted to her, and that was something he could not afford to do.

"You do not have to thank me. Do you want to set a date, or would you like to wait?"

"How about September?"

"That is only three months away," she said, surprised.

"I know your father can get the license early, or is it not enough time to make plans?"

"No, I can do it."

"Where would you like to hold the ceremony?"

"There is this beautiful church here in town. I would like to be married there, if that is okay. I do not know if anyone would travel this far. Of course, we can accommodate most of the guests here. There is also a nice inn in town. Is that all right with you?"

"It sounds good to me. After we solve this issue with Dougal, we can go back and start planning the wedding."

"I want to go tell Mom and Dad."

"Of course."

After Veronica left the room, Owen's smile disappeared. He wanted to stop this horrible plan. Wanted to tell her the truth. She did not deserve what he was going to do. Taking a deep breath, he tried to get ahold of himself. He had to think of his family, his sister, of Ada. She needed him, but he had to put everything out of his head right now. There was a plan that had to go off without a hitch the next day.

Getting up, he squared his shoulders and left the room.

That afternoon, dressed in commoners' clothes, Owen and Gregor waited in the hall for Veronica. She came down the stairs, satchel in one hand, hat in the other, wearing men's clothing. Walking up to Owen, she couldn't help but smile.

"What is with the big smile?"

"I was just thinking how you could look good in a flour sack."

Owen smiled, shaking his head. "The things you say."

"Ready?" asked Gregor.

"Yes," said both Owen and Veronica.

At that time, Henry and Ellen walked up.

"Please, be careful," said Henry as he gave her a hug.

"I will, do not worry."

"We will always worry. It is what parents do," said Ellen, as she also gave her a hug.

Henry walked up to Owen. "Take care of my daughter."

"I will."

"Let us be off," said Gregor.

As they walked to the stables, Owen saw some men bringing out the huge horses with hair covering their hooves.

"Where are the saddles?" asked Owen

"Most farmers can't afford saddles, so we ride without them. Have you ever ridden like this? asked Veronica.

"No, I haven't." He felt very intimidated.

"Don't worry. We will go slow so you can get comfortable."

At first, he was unsure about riding like that, but after a while, he got the hang of it.

Once they arrived at Donaldson's estate, they went to the stables, where they stayed until dark. Liam had his butler sneak them into the house unseen. Veronica saw Seinaid sitting on the couch beside Liam as she walked into the office. Once she saw Veronica, she jumped up and ran to her.

"I have missed you so much," said Seinaid with her thick accent as they hugged.

"I have missed you too."

"Thank you for coming to help. Thank all of you." She had tears in her eyes.

Liam walked up behind Seinaid. "I sent a message this afternoon to Dougal. He should have already sent someone to check the place out for traps." He then looked at Veronica. "I would not have recognized you," he said with a smile.

Owen walked up beside Veronica. She looked at Owen and saw him glare at Liam. "Why don't you men talk strategy while I get caught up with Seinaid?" she said, trying to ease the tension.

"Good idea," said Gregor.

Veronica took Seinaid's arm and walked to the couch, and the men went to the desk. "So, you and Liam?" Asked Veronica, causing Seinaid to lower her head. "It's all right. I think that is terrific."

"It is not acceptable. I am a poor farmer's daughter."

"That will not matter as long as he loves you. Does his age bother you?"

"No, not at all. I truly love him. He is so kind and caring. It took him a long time to get over his wife's death."

"His wife died?" Veronica was shocked that she hadn't heard. She looked over at Liam, and her heart broke for him.

"Yes, in childbirth. The bairn did not survive, as well."

"Oh, I had no idea. How awful."

"Do not say anything, 'cause I have not told him yet, but I am having his bairn," Seinaid whispered.

Veronica smiled. "When all this is over, you need to tell him. And I insist on attending your wedding. I also hope you and Liam will attend mine."

"Who are you marrying?" Veronica nodded toward Owen. "Oh, that tall drink of water?"

They started laughing, and the men stopped talking and looked over.

"There are rooms prepared for the men, but Seinaid insists you stay with her tonight," said Liam.

"It is late, and we need to rest. No telling what time Dougal will arrive. You are sure he will come himself?" asked Owen.

"I am sure. He trusts no one, especially with this much at stake."

"Agreed, let us go, Seinaid. Show me to your room. I need a bath."

Once everyone was in their rooms, Veronica went to her satchel and pulled out a leather pouch. "Seinaid, take this to Liam."

"What is it?"

"Something that I promised him. Tell no one."

"Why the secret?"

"Blackthorn castle is mine, but I need alliances. I know I am getting married, and Owen will be my protection, but it cannot hurt to have eyes around when I am not. There might come a time when I need help. I will take my bath while you are gone."

When Seinaid returned, Veronica noticed she looked strange.

"What's wrong?"

"That was five thousand."

"Yes."

"Veronica, that is a fortune."

"Seinaid, once we stop Dougal, Liam will use it to repair this place and support itself. Besides, I cannot have my godchild living with worried parents. You deserve a good life."

Seinaid hugged her with tears in her eyes. "You are the best."

"Yes, I am." Veronica smiled, then they spent most of the night talking and laughing before finally falling asleep, exhausted.

Early, before the sun was up, everyone was in the dining room eating breakfast.

"How are you going to get him to confess?" asked Owen.

"He is arrogant. I can work with that. Trust me. He loves to brag, thinking he is smarter than everyone else."

"I have to agree. Dougal loves to talk," said, Gregor.

It didn't take long after the sun came up for Dougal to show. Once he had been sighted, Veronica, Owen, and Gregor entered the hidden room, and Liam left it slightly open so everyone could hear clearly.

"Do not make a sound until I open it up."

Dougal and one of his men, who obviously by his look was dangerous, entered the office, and just as Liam said, Dougal's arrogance and pride made him easy to manipulate into bragging about his crimes. He had only brought a few documents he had on Liam's father so he could still force him into compliance.

As they were leaving, the unknown man stopped at the door and looked back, scanning the room as if looking for something. Liam held his breath until the man looked at him, nodded, and left. He waited until his butler notified him that they had left before he opened the bookshelf.

"That worked perfectly. I will go and get some men to help arrest Dougal and his fellow cohorts," said Gregor.

"I hope you find everything he has on my father."

As they talked, Owen noticed Veronica seemed distracted. "What is wrong?"

"I was thinking about something my father always says."

"What is that?"

"That was too easy," she says, looking at him.

"That bothers you?"

"Yes, I do not know why, but it does."

Hearing their conversation, Liam thought about the man with Dougal. "I waited to let you out because a man with him acted as if he knew something was not right. He looked around the office. It made me nervous, but he did not seem to catch on."

"Do you think we should wait a little while before we leave?" asked Owen.

"I am sure they are long gone by now."

At that time, Seinaid walked into the office. "I have your bags waiting."

Veronica walked over and hugged her.

"And your favorite ugly hat."

"Thank you. Walk us to the barn?" she said as she put the hat on, and they both laughed.

Veronica and Seinaid walked to the stable arm and arm while the men followed a few feet behind. Owen thought about riding back without a saddle and had an idea.

"Veronica?"

She stopped right outside the stable doors as Seinaid walked on in. "Yes."

"Do you think we could borrow a saddle from Liam?" He was not embarrassed at all about being spoilt to a saddle.

Veronica smiled, thinking about teasing him, when she noticed him looking behind her as his smile disappeared. She looked back and froze as she saw Dougal holding a knife to Seinaid's throat. Standing to his right was a man holding a pistol.

"Thought you was smart having set me up?"

"Do not hurt her," said Liam as he stepped forward.

"Stay where you are, or the lass gets her throat cut."

Everyone stood still, trying to think of what to do.

"Let her go and take me," said Veronica.

"Now, why would I do that? This one is special to Liam." Dougal ran his finger down the side of her face as tears dripped off her chin.

"If you do not let her go, I will never stop hunting you," said Liam.

"Take me instead," Veronica said again.

"Once again, why would I take a boy?"

"I am not a boy."

"No," said Owen as Veronica took her hat off.

"I am Veronica Aldridge. Remember me? How far do you think you will get around here if you hurt a pregnant woman?" Liam's head snaps to Veronica, then back to Seinaid. "My father will pay anything to get me back safe and sound. Enough to make it easy to disappear."

The corner of his mouth raised in an evil sneer as what she said registered. He was already thinking of the fortune he could get off the wealthy Henry Aldridge. "All right. Walk toward my friend here."

"No, I will walk to you, and you will let her go."

"No, Veronica," said Owen. She could hear the worry in his voice.

Veronica turned back to Owen. "I will be okay," she says, giving him a wink as if she had a plan.

She slowly walked to Dougal, keeping her eyes on him and the man with the pistol. Once she got close, he pushed Seinaid to the ground and grabbed Veronica.

"We are leaving now," said Dougal as they walked back into the stables.

Veronica put her right hand on the arm holding the knife and made a fist with her left. In one swift move, she swung her fist down and twisted the arm that held the knife. When her fist connected to the sensitive parts between his legs, he doubled over, allowing her to escape his hold.

The man saw what happened and pointed the gun in her direction, but Ian jumped out of the shadows and tackled him to the ground before he could fire. At the same time, Aaron grabbed Dougal, and in seconds, it is over.

Liam picked up Seinaid and hugged her as Owen walked to Veronica and turned her to face him.

"Do not ever do that again. Do you hear me? That was reckless and dangerous." She was shocked at how angry he was and couldn't say anything. After a few seconds, he pulled her towards him, wrapping his arms around her in a tight embrace. "You scared me."

"I am sorry. I could not let him take Seinaid. Besides, I knew Ian and Aaron were around somewhere."

Liam pulled back and looked at Seinaid. "Are you pregnant?"

She nodded her head, and he pulled her back into a hug with a smile on his face.

Veronica walked over to them as Owen walked to Ian.

"Thank you both for saving her," Owen says.

"We were hiding in the forest watching when they left. When we saw someone going into the barn, we snuck in behind, but they had already grabbed Seinaid. We were not surprised Lady Veronica traded herself. She has no fear. Always jumping straight into the fight," said Aaron.

"Well, that is going to change."

"Good luck with that," says Ian.

Owen then turned and walked to Veronica as he heard Liam ask Seinaid to marry him, which she agreed.

"When is the ceremony?" asked Veronica.

"What do you say? How soon do you want to get married?"

"Now," replied Seinaid.

"Oh no, you need a dress. The church has to be arranged. Flowers, food for the celebration." Owen grabbed Veronica and put his hand over her mouth to stop her rambling. She looked up at him like he had lost his mind.

"That might be a little much right now," said Liam, a little embarrassed.

"Do not overthink it. We will have the meal at the castle. There are enough flowers in my garden to fill the church, and I know we can find a beautiful dress for you to wear."

"Are ye sure?" asked Liam

"Consider it my wedding gift. Seinaid is one of my best friends, and that is my godchild she is caring. Besides, I want everyone to know we are now friends."

Liam looked at Seinaid for an answer, and she shook her head yes with a smile.

"Umm, maybe we should wait to see if you survive her father. Remember you have to go see them?" said, Veronica.

"Oh, I forgot about that," said Liam, looking nervous.

"A little advice. Save the fact that she is pregnant for last in case they say no. Then, her mother will demand you marry her."

They all laughed except for Veronica, who didn't understand the humor. She was serious.

"Once you get their approval, bring everyone to the castle to stay. Do not worry about anything. I have it handled."

"Are you sure? You don't have to do this," said Seinaid.

"Yes, I cannot wait." Veronica was bouncing with excitement.

Owen watched her and couldn't help but smile. "Let us get going. It sounds like there is a lot to be done."

"Oh, Owen, you can borrow a saddle," said Liam.

"Good man." Owen shook his hand.

Three days later, the wedding was beautiful. The church was full of flowers. The food was prepared, and the entire town showed up. Seinaid was so happy with how everything turned out. Her parents weren't too sure about her marrying a lord, but they agreed wholeheartedly when they heard about the baby.

Liam asked Kieran to stand up with him. Dressed to the nines in the latest fashion, nobody recognized Kieran. People mistook him for a lord as well. With Liam's help, that could come true.

Almost everyone in town was there. Some came for the wedding, but some came to see if it was true that the Donaldson and Brannon clans were becoming friends. After the hundreds of guests left the castle, Owen, Liam, Kieran, and Sean disappeared to the study to relax.

Seinaid's parents went back home, refusing to move to Liam's estate.

"I worry about my parents. I will not be there to help them."

"Do not worry. I have already hired people to help."

"Thank you so much, Veronica. I do not know what I would have done without you," said Seinaid as she hugged her.

"It is getting late. We should get the men and retire for the evening. We will be returning to London tomorrow."

"I will miss you."

"I will be returning soon. Remember, I am getting married in three months."

"Yes, I cannot wait to see you finally married."

"Me too." They laughed as they walked towards the study.

Once they entered, they could tell the men had hit the bourbon way too hard. Liam wrapped his arms around Seinaid, and she had a time controlling his hand as he confessed his undying love.

"I am getting married, everyone," said Owen in a drunken slur. All the men hollered congratulations as they tried to stand but stumbled. Veronica had to call for Ian, William, and Aaron to help get the men to their rooms.

"They will surely feel it in the morning," she said as she watched the men being carried away.

Later that night, she lay in bed thinking about her wedding. She had to start planning as soon as she got back. Finally, she drifted off to sleep, dreaming about the beautiful life she would have with Owen.

The following day, Owen, Kieran, and Sean suffered as they downed several glasses of water. Veronica couldn't help but smile as they moaned.

Seinaid and Liam left early to return home. Liam wanted to get started immediately on the repairs to his estate. He wanted everything to run smoothly before Seinaid was very far along with their child.

After everyone finished eating, they said their goodbyes to Sean and Kieran.

"Henry, can I have a word?" asked Owen.

"Certainly. Veronica and Ellen, would you both check and make sure everything is ready for our departure?"

"Yes, Father," said Veronica as they left the room.

"What did you want to speak about?"

"There are some things I have noticed that I do not understand."

"What are those?"

"The other day, I overheard a maid refer to Veronica as 'your grace'. Then, at the wedding, I noticed people bowing to her."

Henry held up his hand to stop Owen from talking. "Would everyone please leave the room," said Henry to the cleaning servants.

Owen felt something wasn't right for Henry to make everyone leave.

"Since you and Ronnie are going to be married, you should be made aware of some things."

"What things?"

"What do you know of Scotland's royal lineage?"

"Just what I learned in school. I am afraid I did not pay much attention to most of it."

"As you know, the crown went to the house of Bruce, then the Tudors, but there was the house of Balliol. That is the line Veronica is part of."

"Are you saying Veronica is a descendant of Scotland's royalty?"

"Yes."

Owen was shocked; Veronica was royalty.

"Is there a danger to her?"

"No. There is no threat. If there were, Ellis would have the first claim to Scotland's crown. It is the responsibility that comes with this place that bothers me," said Henry as he motioned around the room. "Even today, if there is a conflict and the magistrate can't solve it, they will come here to get justice."

"Are you saying Veronica would make decisions that the people would obey?"

"She already has been in that position. What I am going to tell you can go no further. Ellis does not even know."

## Three years earlier,

"Ronnie, I need you to attend a meeting. There is a serious problem between the two clans. I think this is a good time for you to use your training," said Tyrin as he walked up to Veronica. They were sitting in the dayroom when Tyrin received a letter from the magistrate.

Henry was reading a paper, listening to Tyrin.

"No. She is too young to have that kind of responsibility," Henry said as he put down the paper.

"She might be your daughter, but she is my granddaughter and needs to be seen in the position she was born to be in. If it eases your mind, you can attend. But stay in a corner and say nothing. It will not sit well with the clans to have a sassenach in Shield Hall."

Veronica was nervous and excited to see her grandfather as a leader. "I want to be there," she said.

Henry looked toward Ellen, wanting her opinion.

"I think she should attend. She needs the experience."

"I always liked you, lass. A smart head on your shoulders," said Tyrin, looking at Ellen.

She smiled and looked at Veronica. "You need to come with me and get changed. The first time being presented, you need to look at the part of your station." Ellen stood and escorted Veronica out. "Henry, there is more than training for why I want Ronnie to attend. A lass has been hurt badly, and it might make her more at ease if another lass is there."

Henry thought for a moment and nodded his head in understanding.

That afternoon, Veronica and Ellen came down the stairs. Veronica wore a royal blue dress with intricate beaded designs in silver on the bodice and a square neckline and long sleeves with the same beaded design on the cuffs. Across her chest was the Brannon tartan in dark blue and deep red. Her grandfather was proud of her choice.

Henry stood in awe at how grown-up and regal she looked. "You look like a princess. Your mother would be so proud of you." He hugged her.

"Aye. On that, we agree," said Tyrin as his eyes glazed over with tears at the mention of his daughter. "You look beautiful," he said as he held out his arm for her to take.

Henry followed behind them as they entered Shield Hall. Both the clans were already there and on opposite sides of the room. You could feel the tension in the room as they walked toward the front.

As Tyrin sat down, the clans came towards him. Veronica stood to his right with her head high. Henry stood in the corner behind them, watching her. She truly looked like she belonged there.

"Why is there a sassenach in here?" asked a big burly-looking man.

"I wish to show this Englishman Scottish justice when English law fails us," said Tyrin.

The rest of the men in the room shook their heads in agreement.

"Now, I wish to hear from the clan Donnachaidh."

A tall man stepped forward. Veronica noticed behind him was a young girl that held her head down. Even at a distance, she could see bruises on her face.

"I am Aiden, the leader of my clan. My daughter Beatrice was attacked a week ago in a field on her way home."

"And who did she say it was?"

"Eachann, the leader of the McMillan clan."

"She lies," said the burly man from before.

Both clans started hollering at each other.

"ENOUGH," yelled Tyrin, and everyone grew quiet.

Veronica walked down the steps toward the girl that was standing behind Aiden. They all watched as Veronica approached the girl and stopped in front of her.

"Are you Beatrice?" she asked in a soft voice.

She shakes her head yes but doesn't look up.

"Do not look down. You have nothing to be ashamed of. You did nothing wrong." Beatrice slowly raised her head, and Veronica had to remain calm as she saw the extent of her injuries. Her face was black and blue, even her neck, where it looked like he had tried to strangle her. "He did this to you?"

"Aye," she said in a whisper.

As Veronica looked her over, she saw something under her sleeve about midway down her arm. "May I?" she asked as she pointed to her arm.

Tyrin sat and watched Veronica, wondering what she was doing as she raised the girl's sleeve and studied her arm. She let her arm go and turned to walk toward the other clan.

"Are you, Eachann?" she asked, stopping before the man who had called Beatrice a liar.

"Aye."

"You wouldn't mind showing me your teeth?"

He did not say a word; he just looked at Veronica. A young man standing to his left stepped forward.

"Why do you need to see his teeth?"

"The one who hurt Beatrice is missing teeth here," she said as she pointed to the right side of her face. The man then looked at Eachann with wide eyes.

"You did it. Did you not?" asked Veronica as a corner of her mouth raised.

He grew furious at being caught by her. "You English bitch." He pulled a dagger from his back and lunged at Veronica.

Tyrin jumped from his chair, and Henry propelled himself off the wall he was leaning on. But they both stopped in shock when they saw the dagger buried in Eachann chest. In an instant, Veronica had taken the dagger away from him and plunged it into his chest, straight through his heart.

"How dare you attack me in my own home," said Veronica with so much anger. "You will never hurt another girl."

Eachann looked down at the dagger that was impaled to the hilt in his chest and fell dead to the ground.

Nobody moved or spoke.

"Did he have any sons?" asked Veronica as she looked at the man standing in front of her.

"I am David, his oldest."

"Do you believe he hurt Beatrice?"

"He is missing teeth," he said, looking down at his father.

"Do not be ashamed. You are not your father."

"He must have been the one who hurt my Mary," said a man that stood towards the back of the group.

"Were there more girls hurt?"

"Aye. We had two lasses killed but never knew who it was," said David.

"You are now the leader of your clan. I hope you are a better man than he was," said Veronica, looking at David.

"He is a good man," said a man, and the rest nodded their heads in agreement.

She turned and walked back toward Beatrice. "Do you feel justice has been done?"

"Aye," said Beatrice, eyes still wide from what she just witnessed.

Tyrin returned to his seat and decided to let her finish. Veronica then looked at the rest of the clan and saw them nod their heads in satisfaction. She walked a few steps back to face both clans.

"He called me an English bitch," she said as she pointed to the man lying dead on the floor. "My father is English, but my mother was Leah

Brannon, and I am Tyrin Brannon's granddaughter. This is my home, and I swear my allegiance to Scotland and its people." As she spoke, she looked at everyone in the room. "If anyone here does not wish for me to sit in this chair," she pointed toward where Tyrin sat, "then say so now."

Nobody moved or said a word.

"I promise you all justice will be swift, and I will stand beside the strongest of you." She looked at Beatrice. "And the weakest. I have Scottish blood running through my veins, and I will defend my people with my dying breath," she said with a firm voice.

"You have our fealty," said Aiden as he and his clan took a knee.

"And ours," said David as everyone went down on their knees.

Tyrin smiled big with pride as he watched everyone pledge their allegiance to Veronica. She had taken a life and still stood with her head high, showing no weakness.

Henry still stood where he had, frozen as he watched his daughter. *She should have been a queen,* he thought.

Owen sat, not saying a word as Henry told the story.

"Veronica killed a man. That explains why she was staring at the floor in Shield Hall," he said in a low voice, talking to himself, but Henry still heard him.

"Even though she acted like it didn't bother her, I knew it did. After everyone left, she went to her room. I told Ellen, and she went to check on her. Found her crying. I ask you not to say anything to Veronica. It took some time for her to forget what happened."

"I will not. Thank you for telling me."

Owen stood and left to prepare to leave for England. His thoughts were about Veronica. How she had always seemed ordinary but was anything but.

# CHAPTER TWELVE

The truth is not always beautiful,
nor beautiful words, the truth

Lao T

Once everyone was back in London, Owen went to inform his parents that he would be getting married in three months. Both were extremely happy, of course, for different reasons.

Veronica's first visit was to Hannah. Complete silence was not the reaction she expected after telling her of her marriage to Owen.

"Did you hear me?"

"Yes, I am sorry. That was the last thing I was expecting."

At that time, Hannah's mother, Lady Eleanor, walked in, reading the paper. "Hannah, you will not believe whom Veronica is marrying?"

"It is already in the paper?" asked Hannah, surprised.

"Yes, as soon as we agreed, Father sent someone to the paper."

Eleanor looked up and saw Veronica sitting there.

"Oh, Veronica, I did not know you were here. Congratulations on your upcoming nuptials."

"Thank you, Lady Eleanor. I hope you will be able to travel to my home in Scotland. That is where the ceremony will be held."

"Of course. We would not miss it," said Eleanor as she walked to Veronica, hugging her.

Hannah was quiet, not knowing what to say.

"I know what you are thinking. Yes, part of Owen's reason is because of his family's situation. We discussed this and got to know each other these past few days. I think we could be happy."

Hannah smiled and got up, walking to Veronica sitting beside her. "Then I am happy for you."

They let out a squeal and hugged each other.

"We are having a wedding. This is going to be so much fun," said, Hannah.

The rest of the day, they discussed plans and made appointments. By the time Veronica got home, she was mentally tired but still needed to talk to her mother and review her decisions.

The next day, Owen was in a carriage, waiting for Ada. Once she entered, they hugged and kissed passionately.

"I have missed you so much," said Ada.

"I missed you too."

"Mother read in the paper that you have succeeded."

"Yes," he said, looking away.

"Owen, I know this is very unsettling, but you have saved me. Mother has agreed to wait. She is not forcing me to accept other suiters anymore."

That made Owen relax. He did love Ada and couldn't stand the idea of her being in the arms of another man. She knew he had to keep Owen on the right path, and there was one way she knew she had the power. It didn't take much effort before she straddled him. It wasn't the first time for her to have sex. Not even the first time in a carriage.

Once they had righted their clothes, Owen started feeling guilty.

"We can't do this anymore until this is over."

"You are right. We cannot risk getting caught. Where is the ceremony taking place?"

"At a church in Scotland. The wedding breakfast will be at her castle."

"Castle?"

"Yes, Veronica has a castle. Her grandfather left two estates to his grandchildren. Ellis got one, and Veronica got the other, which happened to be a castle. A giant castle."

Jealousy engulfed Ada. It was bad enough that she had that house on Broad's Street. Now, she had a castle. She couldn't wait until the plan would be done, and Veronica was ultimately humiliated.

"Are you okay?" Owen asked, noticing how quiet she was.

"Yes, just thinking about when this is all over, and we can be together," she says, wrapping her arms around him.

"Yes, me too. I need to go. Our families are getting together for dinner to go over the wedding and discuss the marriage agreement."

That made Ada happy, thinking about the amount of money in that agreement. She kissed him and exited the carriage.

Owen closed his eyes and laid his head back. Sometimes, he felt like he was suffocating. Wanting to pray to God for help but knowing he couldn't deal with what he was doing, he was on his own.

That night at the dinner table, everyone paired off, talking. Ann and Ellen were lost in conversation while Henry and Callum did the same. At the other end, Owen and Veronica sat watching their parents.

"Do you think they will ask what we think?" asked Owen.

"No." Veronica smiled.

"How are the arrangements going?"

"Everything has been decided."

"Really, in two days? I am impressed," replied Owen.

"Yes, the dress is being made. Flowers have been arranged. The food we will be serving has been decided. Mother and Father are deciding whom to invite, so all I have to do is wait. Have you decided on your wedding clothes?" asked Veronica.

"Yes, I did that yesterday."

The conversation was interrupted when the dining room door opened.

"Did anyone miss me?"

"Ellis, you are home," said Veronica as she jumped up and ran to her brother.

He grabbed her in a hug and spun her around.

"How is my little sister?" he asked as he sat her down.

Henry and Ellen walked over, and he hugged both of them.

"You are back a week early," says Henry.

"As soon as you sent word that Owen asked for my sister, I made arrangements to come home." Noticing Owen standing at the end of the table, he walked over and stood in front of him, looking mad. "So, you want to marry my little sister?"

"She already said yes," replied Owen with a grimace.

Ellis stood still, looking at Owen as his mouth slowly started making a grin. "That is fantastic." They both laughed and hugged. "I couldn't ask for a better man to marry my sister."

Once they parted, Ellis walked over to Callum.

"Ellis, good to see you."

"Lord Pierce, good to see you and Lady Ann." He shook Callum's hand.

"Ellis," replied Ann as she nodded her head.

"Come sit. We were discussing the wedding," said Henry.

the rest of the night was filled with laughter and happiness.

Once everyone left, Ellis went to the nursery to see his little brother. He stood at the crib and watched him sleep. After he left the room, he saw his family waiting for him.

"He has grown so much," he said as he shut the door.

"Yes, he will be so happy to see you," said Ellen.

"It is late, and we need to get some rest. The past few days have been hectic," said Henry.

"Yes, but first, I want to talk to my baby sister." Ellis grabbed Veronica's hand, leading her to his room.

Ellen and Henry smiled as they watched them walk away.

"It's good to have him home," said Ellen.

"Yes, it is." Henry put his arm around his wife, and they walked to their room.

"So, tell me, how have things been?" asked Ellis as they sat by the fire.

"It has been so hard. After you left, things changed."

"What happened after I left?"

"You being gone, people did not have to be friendly to me. You know most of the girls were nice to me to get close to you."

"Yes, I know that was probably true. I am sorry."

"It is not your fault. You cannot help being so handsome." She smiled.

"That is true," he said with a grin.

Veronica picked up a small pillow and threw it at him. He laughed and threw it back.

"So, tell me, how do you feel about Owen?"

"At first, I did not know how to feel. I thought it was an awful joke. Did you know his family is in financial ruin?"

"What! Is that why he is marrying you?" Ellis got up, showing how upset he was.

"Ellis, sit down. We have already discussed this. Besides, father has been helping them. But, after Agnes stopped his attempt to court Ada, he decided he needed somebody more his equal," she said with a grin.

'I have to admit, I'm so glad he did not marry Ada. I tried to talk to him so many times about her, but he would never listen."

"You do not like Ada? I thought all men liked her."

"She is not the lady she pretends to be," Ellis said as he remembered when Ada tried to seduce him, and when she failed, she started after Owen. "Veronica, will you be happy with him?"

"I think so. We have spent some interesting time together."

"Tell me."

Veronica told him everything that had happened in the last month.

"I did not start training you to fight so you could put yourself in harm's way. You are lucky you did not get killed. I am surprised Father did not lose his temper over what happened at Lord Donaldson's home. Or does he not know?"

"I did not tell him. With Seinaid's wedding, everyone was so busy getting things ready."

"I see."

They were quiet for a few minutes.

"Is Lydia still your maid?"

"Yes. She and Adrian are together now."

"That makes sense. You have been a godsend for so many people."

"I am just glad I could help them."

"You are an incredible woman, little sister. But I insist you stop. You are getting married, and maybe will have a family of your own."

"I know. I do not think Owen would understand my late-night excursions."

"Well, I guess we had better get to bed," said Ellis.

They got up, and he walked her to the door.

"Oh, Hannah has not accepted any offers yet," she says as she leaves the room.

He stood there thinking about what she said. He smiled; his little sister knew him better than he thought. Maybe it was time he settled down too.

A couple of days later, Hannah came to the house to attend a dress fitting with Veronica. As she removed her cloak, she did not notice Ellis walking up behind her. When she turned around, she froze.

"Lady Hannah, it is a pleasure to see you again." He took her hand and kisses her fingers.

Veronica walked up, seeing Hannah in shock and unable to speak. Hannah had loved Ellis all her life, but he was a rake and would not settle down. Veronica held back from laughing and decided to help her friend.

"Hannah, Ellis got back last night, surprising all of us." That seemed to bring her back to her senses.

"Yes, it is good to see you again, Lord Aldridge," she said, not taking her eyes off him. He smiled at her, which made her heart beat faster. She had always tried to hide how she felt about him, but people could see it in her eyes that she was caught off guard.

"You ready to go? asked Veronica, wanting to save her friend from further embarrassment.

"Uh, yes," she said, finally taking her eyes off him.

"Have a good time, little sister," said Ellis as he kissed her on the cheek.

"I will be home as soon as the fitting is over."

Once they entered the carriage, Hannah put her face in her hands. "I am mortified. I acted like a brainless chit."

"It was adorable. Did you see how he smiled at you?"

"He probably thinks I have something wrong with my brain."

Veronica laughed.

"It is not funny."

"I am sorry. We need to make you look beautiful at my wedding."

"If that would do any good."

"You might be surprised."

"When is Dinah coming back?" says Hannah, changing the subject.

"Owen promised she would be back in time for the wedding. I was hoping she could be with us, but I guess I understand not wanting to be around society right now."

"Once you are married, their situation will change, right?"

"Yes, I am sure it will not take long to improve. I need your help picking out a dress for her. You two are almost the same size," said Veronica.

"Yes, I think that is a wonderful idea."

# CHAPTER THIRTEEN

They muddy the water too
make it seem deep.

Friedrich Nietzsche

On the way home, Veronica stared off in deep thought. As the wedding date got closer, the more uncomfortable she got. The wedding night still bothered her even though Ellen had explained a long time ago what would take place. She couldn't help but think about the whispers she had overheard from other women.

Finally, making a decision, she opened the window and told the driver, James, to stop the carriage. Once stopped, she stuck her head out and told the footman, Phillip, an address she wished to go.

He looked at her, shocked. "I do not think your father will approve, miss."

"You can either take me, or I will go by myself." She stared at him as she waited for an answer.

Phillip looked at James, took a deep breath, then turned around to get back up in his seat. She smiled and sat back. Not long after, they stopped in front of a house. She exited with the hood of her cloak up.

"My lady, we should not be here. What if someone sees you?" James asked.

"The carriage does not have the crest on the side. Do not worry. I will be fine."

James and Phillip stared at each other. Phillip shrugged his shoulders, and James shut the door. Neither one understood why Veronica would go to that part of town. It wasn't a bad place, just well-known for gambling clubs and homes where men kept their mistresses.

Veronica walked up and knocked on the door. A butler answered and was surprised to see a young girl standing there.

"How may I help you?"

"Veronica Aldridge to see Lady Beauchamp."

"Please, come in." He stepped aside to let her in. "I'll inform the madam."

As Veronica removed her cloak, she saw a woman walked up. She was tall with light brown hair and hazel eyes. Veronica could see why men would want her as a mistress, for she was beautiful, and the French accent just added to the appeal.

"How can I help you, Miss Aldridge?"

"Please, just Veronica," she said with a smile. "I would like to speak with you in private if that is all right, Lady Beauchamp?"

"Of course, and just Angelique. This way. Have Annie bring tea," Angelique said to her butler.

As they stepped into the crimson drawing room, Veronica noticed another woman sitting on the couch. She was blonde, blue-eyed, and also beautiful. Veronica assumed she was also a mistress.

"Veronica, this is Audrey Herring. She lives here with me. Audrey, this is Veronica Aldridge."

Audrey's head snapped to Veronica in apparent surprise.

"Hello, it is a pleasure to meet you," Veronica said, smiling.

"Hello," replied Audrey.

"What brings you here?" asked Angelique.

"I need some advice. Actually, information of the personal kind," Veronica said, blushing.

"Maybe I should step out," said Audrey.

"No, stay if you don't mind." Veronica thought as a mistress, she could also have advice.

"All right."

"What kind of information could I possibly help you with?" asked Angelique.

"There are some things I would like to know about between a man and a woman," said Veronica, looking down.

"Oh, you are getting married soon," said Audrey as she realized what she was asking. "Is Lady Ellen not your mother? She has not explained things to you?"

"Yes, she has explained the marriage bed, but I have heard conversations of different situations I do not understand," she said, blushing.

Audrey reached over and patted Veronica's hand. "It is okay. Do not be embarrassed. We will help you," she said with a smile.

"You are marrying Owen Pierce," said Angelique.

"Yes, forgive me, but I have heard you were once his mistress."

"I was more his teacher. How do you know this?"

"His sister, Dinah. She has an uncanny ability to find things out." Veronica smiled, thinking about Dinah always knowing secrets. "What do you mean by a teacher?"

"Owen wanted to learn how to please a woman. He was not interested in his pleasure." They all got quiet as Annie brought the tea and set it on the table. Once she left, Audrey started pouring. "You want to know how to please him?" asked Angelique.

"Yes," said Veronica, blushing.

"Do not be embarrassed. It is perfectly normal to want to prepare for this kind of thing," said Audrey.

For an hour, the three women talked. Veronica blushed several times, causing the women to laugh but making her feel at ease.

The two women walked her to the door when it was time to leave. After she donned her cloak, Veronica turned and hugged both women.

"Thank you both so much."

"Veronica, tell Lady Ellen that Meredith Ferguson said hello," Audrey said.

"Meredith Ferguson?"

"Yes, she is an old friend."

"All right, I will," Veronica replied.

"Veronica, be careful," said Angelique.

"I will," she replied and walked out the door.

The women watched as she entered the carriage.

"She is different," said Angelique.

"How so?"

"Never have I had a socialite treat me with such kindness."

"Yes, she is a sweet child."

"Why did you not tell her about what Agnes was planning?" asked Angelique.

"How would I explain how I knew, reveal my spy in Agnes's home? Besides, I am not going to be the one to hurt her."

"It will destroy her," said Angelique.

"No, she is strong. It will do some damage, but she will survive," Audrey said as she walked away. She stopped and turned to look back at her. "But Agnes won't."

"We will make sure of it," replied Angelique, smiling.

When Veronica got back home, Ellen was waiting on her.

"We will be leaving in the morning."

"Why so soon? The wedding is still a month away. My dress has yet to be finished," Veronica said, surprised.

"We have already received most of the invitation acceptance letters. Everyone is coming, and I mean most of England."

"Seriously?" Replied Veronica, thinking she was exaggerating.

"Veronica, I am dead serious. We have to get to Blackthorn and help hire more staff. The entire castle will be full of guests, and so will the White Heart Inn in town."

Realizing her mother was not joking, she became nervous. "Mum, I am not so sure about this. What if something happens? What if Owen changes his mind? What if I embarrass the family? Maybe I should rethink getting married?"

Hearing Veronica rambling, she walked over to her and took her in her arms. "Sweet girl, he will not change his mind. It will be perfect, and you will be a beautiful bride."

"You think so? You are not just saying that?" Tears formed in her eyes.

"I know so. Now go and help Lydia load your trunk," said Ellen as she hurried Veronica up the stairs.

Ellen stopped smiling once she was gone, thinking how she will kill Owen if he doesn't show. Henry and Ellis decided to stay behind and would join them later.

Owen was there the next morning to see Veronica off, because Ellen sent word that she was getting nervous.

He stood outside by the carriage with everyone as they prepared to leave.

"I will see you in two weeks," said Owen.

"You promise?" asked Veronica.

"I promise," he said as he hugged her.

"All right, that's enough," Ellis said as he walked up. "You be careful, little sister. And make sure everything is just the way you want it." He hugged her, then patted her on the head.

"I love you, big brother."

"Of course you do. I'm the best brother anyone could ask for." He grinned.

"And the humblest," Veronica said, smiling as she entered the carriage behind Ellen.

Two weeks before the wedding, Dinah arrived home, just finding out about Owen's engagement to her friend.

"Where is my mother?" she asked the butler.

"In the sitting room."

Ann looked up from her embroidery to see Dinah walk in. "Dinah, I am glad you are home."

"You want to tell me what is going on?"

"About what?"

"Owen marrying Veronica."

"Your brother is marrying Veronica. What more do you need to know?"

"Then why was I not told until now? I know something is not right with this marriage."

"You do not need to worry about it. Everything is as it should be," she says, not looking at her.

"Mother, tell me the truth. Why is Owen marrying Veronica?"

"He decided she was a better fit," said Ann as she walked off, hoping Dinah would drop it.

"Better fit? He never showed her any interest. What about Ada?" she asked as she followed her mother.

"It did not work out."

"Mother, stop!" Dinah hollered.

Ann stopped and turned around. "Dinah, just be glad Veronica is getting married." She turned back around to leave, then stopped again. "Tomorrow, you need to go to a fitting. Veronica had you a dress designed for the wedding."

"Mother, I will find out what you are keeping from me." She turned and walked to her room.

The next day, Dinah went for her fitting. As she was leaving, Ada walked in.

"Hello, Dinah."

"Ada." Dinah continued walking. She never liked Ada and always tried to avoid her when possible.

"I guess congratulations are in order," said Ada.

Dinah stopped and turned back around. "You are not upset over losing Owen?"

"No, in fact, my family and I will be attending the wedding."

"Why would you go? You did everything you could to get my brother, and now you act like everything is great. What is going on?"

"I do not know what you are talking about."

Dinah had an idea. She knew Ada was arrogant and could be goaded into spilling what she knew. "Well, at least I do not have to make polite conversation with you anymore. And I am so glad I do not have to watch you with my brother. You were never worthy of him," she said, holding her head high.

"I would not act all smug, Dinah. Once I marry your brother, things will change. You will be lucky to set foot in my house," Ada said in a low voice.

"Once you marry Owen? Are you delusional? Owen will be Veronica's husband."

"For now, but you never know what might happen later. They could get divorced after your family's financial situation is resolved."

Dinah felt like her heart had stopped. "Owen would never do something so heinous."

"Really, not even to protect his family?" She could see the pride on Ada's face. "If I were you, I would keep quiet and not say anything to anybody. I cannot wait till they are married."

Dinah knew Ada had just told her the truth. She left the store in a hurry, leaving Ada to gloat.

As soon as Dinah got home, she found her mother in her bedroom. "Mother."

Ann looked up and sees Dinah standing there with tears on her face. "What is wrong?" she asked as she got up and walked to Dinah.

"Owen is marrying my best friend to divorce her as soon as he has her money."

Ann looked away. "How did you find out?"

"I was hoping you would say it was not true. How am I supposed to stand by and allow this to happen?"

Ann walked up and grabbed her arms. "You will if you want us to survive. Agnes threatened to tell everyone of our situation if Owen did not marry Veronica."

"I do not care. This is wrong."

"Do you want to see your father humiliated? Do you ever want to get married? Do you want to see me ostracized by everyone?" Ann tightened her grip as she yelled at Dinah.

"No, but why did it have to be Veronica? There were plenty of other heiresses he could have married."

"I do not know. There are other dowrys that match hers." Ann let go of her arms and walked off. "Mother, what do I do?" she asked as tears streamed down her face.

"We will not leave for Edinburgh for another week. Take the time to calm down. Once we get there, talk to your brother but say nothing to your father. He knows nothing of this plan."

"Where is Owen?"

"He has already left with Ellis and Henry."

She turned around and left her mother's room, knowing she would get nowhere with her. It was Owen she needed to talk to, and she would as soon as she got there. He had to stop the plan no matter what happened.

A few days later, Dinah and her family left for the wedding. Callum noticed Dinah seemed troubled by something.

"Dinah, what is on your mind?"

She looked at her father, and for a second, she wanted to tell him the truth but decided not to. "Just the wedding. It is hard to believe that Owen is marrying my friend."

Ann tensed, afraid Dinah would tell him.

"I know, I was surprised when he told me his intentions, but I could not be happier. Veronica is an excellent choice."

When they reached the castle, Dinah stood in awe. She had been there once years ago, but it amazed her still. Once they left the carriage, they saw the courtyard bustling with people. As they entered through the enormous doors, Dinah was lost in the grandeur of the place and did not see her friends.

"Dinah." Hearing her name, she saw Hannah and Veronica smiling at her. Tears well in her eyes as she walked up to them and hugged Veronica. She started crying harder as she hugged her tighter. Veronica patted her on the back as she looked at Hannah with a confused, worried, 'what is going on' expression. Hannah shrugged her shoulders, not knowing what was wrong.

"Dinah, are you okay?" asked Veronica.

She let go and backed away, wiping her tears. "I do not know what is wrong with me," Dinah says, taking a deep breath, trying to get control of her emotions.

At that time, Owen walked up. "Hello, sister. How was the trip?"

She turned to look at him, and his smile faded as he saw her tear-stained face.

"Come, let us talk," he said as he wrapped his arm around her shoulder, leading her away.

"What was that about? I have never seen her emotional," said Veronica.

"Maybe everything has been too much for her. We will find out. Right now, we have a bigger problem. Ada and her family just showed up."

"WHAT! Veronica said and then grabbed Hannah and walked off. She refuses to entertain Ada.

At the front door, Henry and Ellen were welcoming guests when she saw Agnes.

"You invited her?"

"You know Thomas is my friend and used to be yours. I could not ask him to come alone."

"I could have."

"Please, sweetheart. You can get along for a couple of days. This is our daughter's wedding."

"I will tolerate her for Veronica, but you will pay later," Ellen said as she turned and left.

Henry let out a breath and turned to greet the Kingsleys. "Thomas, good to see you," he said as he shook his hand.

Owen took Dinah to his room. Sitting on the couch, no one spoke. Finally, Dinah turned to Owen.

"How could you? How could you do something so horrible to a good person?"

"Do you think I want to do this? I have no choice."

"You could have said no."

"And what then, Dinah? Let our family fall? No, I cannot let that happen."

"There has to be another way besides using the best person I know. Veronica has never hurt anybody. There has to be a reason they picked her, other than her dowry."

'I do not know why, but you are right. Veronica is sweet. She is brave and brilliant." Dinah watched Owen as he talked about Veronica and everything they had been through. There was a light in his eyes that he did not realize, but Dinah saw it.

"I will stay quiet on one condition."

"What is that?"

"Be respectful to her while you are married and give her a happy few months of marriage before you break her heart. Can you do that?"

"Yes, I can do that. I really do enjoy being around her. I have never been around a woman like her."

Dinah got up and walked to the door.

"Do you hate me?" Owen asked.

"No, I do not hate you. I just do not know what I feel right now." She then left the room, never looking back.

The urge to get on a horse and ride away was great, but he couldn't stop now, even if it cost him the love of his sister.

The night before the wedding, the great hall was filled with people eating. Owen, Dinah, and Hannah were there with their families, while Veronica and her family were in a smaller dining room. The servants usually used it, but Henry wanted to have a quiet family meal before Veronica got married.

"Oh, I completely forgot. Meredith Ferguson said hello."

Henry and Ellen froze.

"Who did you say?" asked Ellen.

"Meredith Ferguson."

"When did you see her?" Henry asked.

"When I went to my last dress fitting. I met a woman named Audrey Herring, and she was the one that said her name."

"Where exactly did you see her?"

Veronica looked down. "In town."

Henry could tell something wasn't right and knew Veronica was trying to avoid the question. James was standing at the door, not wanting to tell on Veronica. He decided to try and leave.

"James, stop," Henry said.

He stopped and turned around, looking at Veronica with a sad expression. She smiled at him, letting him know it was okay.

'Where did Veronica go that day?"

"To the Gaming Club District."

"WHAT! Why did you go there?" Henry asked.

Ellis started coughing and looked at his sister with an amused expression. *Leave it to Veronica to bring the entertainment,* he thought.

"I needed to speak to Angelique Beauchamp," she said, not looking up.

Ellis knew Angelique had been Owen's mistress and thought that should be handled by Ellen, not his father.

"Dad, why not let Mother handle this?"

"Yes, honey, calm down and let me handle this," Ellen said.

"Calm down? Our daughter went to see a mistress. What if someone saw her?"

"I know, calm down," Ellen said, then looked at Veronica. "Why did you go there?"

"I needed some questions answered," she said, blushing.

"What could you have learned from her that your mother could not answer?" Henry asked.

"Mother was not Owen's mistress," Veronica said, just loud enough to be heard.

Henry was stunned and didn't know what to say, while Ellis tried hard not to erupt into laughter. Veronica was the only one who could make their father blush.

*I love my sister,* thought Ellis.

"Maybe I should let you handle this," Henry said, looking at Ellen.

"I think that is a wise decision." Ellen patted his hand.

Once they had left the room, Veronica opened up and told Ellen why she had gone to see Angelique. Ellen understood but hoped, in the future, she would come to her instead. Veronica was glad Ellen wasn't mad and that she would make her father understand and not be angry.

Once done talking, Ellen sent Veronica to bed while she sat there trying to think of a way to tell Henry. Most men didn't want to hear about their little girl and sex, so she hoped he wouldn't ask too much.

*I had better get this over with,* she thought as she left the dining room. Then track down James to get the address where Veronica was.

She had an Audrey Herring to track down.

# CHAPTER FOURTEEN

As sure as God made black
and white, what is done in
the dark will come to light.

Johnny Cash

The wedding day had finally arrived, and everyone was busy with final preparations. Owen and Ellis were finished and ready to leave when Henry came in.

"Owen, I was wondering about the ring."

"I have it," said Ellis, pulling it out of his vest pocket.

"I would like to know if you would give her this one instead. I gave it to Leah when Veronica was born."

Owen took the ring and was amazed. It was a gold band with a large ruby. On each side were two rolls of tiny diamonds. "It is beautiful," said Owen.

Ellis walked up beside him to take a look. "I think I remember her wearing this."

"There is an inscription on the inside," Henry said.

"'Always Loved,'" Owen read and looked up at Henry.

"I would catch Leah looking at it occasionally, which always made her smile. So, it would mean a lot to me if you would use it today."

"Yes, of course. Thank you," Owen said as he handed it to Ellis to hold for the ceremony.

"You boys ready to leave?"

"Yes, we are leaving now," Ellis said.

"Good, I will go and see Veronica," Henry said as he left the room.

One floor up, Hannah, Dinah, and Ellen were finishing up. They stepped back to look, and tears formed in Ellen's eyes.

"You look beautiful," she said.

"Thank you, Mother, but I think you three are the beautiful ones today."

Ellen turns her around to face the mirror. Veronica looked and did not recognize the girl staring back. Both sides of her hair were pulled up and pinned in white flowers. The back was down in a cascade of curls. A light amount of powder on her face with just a little color on her cheeks gave a blushing effect. They used a coral color on her lips, providing a natural look.

Ellen gave her a beautiful set of pearls that hung around her neck. White gloves that reached just past her elbow. The dress was light blue, off-the-shoulder, trimmed with delicate white lace, and beautiful embroidery designs on the fitted bodice. The full skirt was split down the center with layers of white lace. Blue ribbon was laced down the back, stopping at her waist in a big bow. The back of the skirt was also split, starting at the bow layers of white lace that extended down her four-foot train. It was a dress a queen would envy.

They heard a knock, and Hannah opened the door, letting Henry in.

He stood there with tears in his eyes as he looked at his little girl, all grown up. "I cannot believe you are getting married today," he said as he hugged her. He pulled back and took a breath. "You ready to leave for the church?"

"Yes, I believe we are," Veronica said with a smile.

"Where is Lucien? Is he Ready?" asked Henry.

"I will go get him and meet you at the carriage," Ellen said as she left.

"Girls, do you mind giving me a minute with my daughter?"

"Of course. We will be in the carriage," said Dinah as they left the room.

"I can stop this right now. It is not too late," Henry said.

Veronica smiled and walked to her father and hugged him. Then, she backed up and saw tears in his eyes. "This is my chance. Owen is a good man. I could not ask for anyone better, and I love him."

Henry smiled. "That is all I needed to hear. Let us go and get married."

She reached down and picked up the end of her train, where she put her hand through a loop that was sewn in. "I am ready," she said as she grabbed his arm.

Veronica saw two carriages; the first would take her family and friends, and the second she and her father. She smiled as she saw two grey horses hooked to her carriage.

"I did not think you believed in superstitions. Especially Scotland's."

"I do not, but I am not going to risk my daughter's happiness."

"I am guessing there will be two white horses after I am married."

Henry looked away, a little uncomfortable. "Maybe."

"Thank you, Father."

He looked at her and smiled. "Anything for my little girl."

She wiped the corner of her eye when a tear threatened to fall.

"No crying. This is a happy day."

She took a deep breath and smiled at him, so thankful to God for giving her that man for a father.

After arriving at the church, Lucien ran up to Veronica. "Sissy, you look pretty."

She kneeled and hugged him.

"Thank you. I love you, Lucien."

"Love you too."

Ellen walked up, took his hand, and led them inside the church. Once inside, bells pealed forth, letting everyone know the bride had arrived, and the ceremony was to begin.

Owen and Ellis step up on the platform as everyone settles in the pews. Owen looked at the overfilled rows and the balcony where the servants from Henry and Veronica's houses stood. Railbert was there with his brother, and you could tell the difference between the two. Ailbert had a big grin, while Railbert had his usual scowl.

What Owen didn't see was Lydia and Adrian hiding in the corner. They should not have come with the risk of someone from England recognizing them, but they couldn't miss Veronica's wedding.

After Hannah and Dinah fixed the train and ensured Veronica's hair and dress were perfect, they went through the doors, taking Lucien with them. Ellis saw Hannah coming down the aisle, and he stopped breathing. She was beautiful, and he couldn't take his eyes off her. Glancing up at him, she blushed and looked away as she sat on the front pews.

Dinah looked at her brother and gave him a smile that did not reach her eyes. He looked out, not wanting to see the disappointment he knew she felt.

Ellen stepped in front of Veronica and took her hands. "I love you, Ronnie," she said as she kissed her cheek.

"I love you too, Mother."

She then walked to the double doors where two men are waiting, opening them to let her in. As she walked down the aisle, she nodded to a man holding a violin in the corner, and he started playing a soft tune.

Hearing the music, Henry held out his arm for Veronica. "I wish your mother could have been here. She would have been so proud of you," he said, trying to keep his voice from cracking.

"She would have been proud of you, too. Since she could not be with us, you gave Ellis and me the perfect mother." Henry looked at Veronica and kissed her cheek.

She took a deep breath, and they started walking to the doors. As they make their way down the aisle, you could see the surprise on their faces—some over the dress but mostly over how Veronica looked.

As the majority of women were envious, one was enraged. Ada did not expect Veronica to look as pretty as she did, but what disturbed her the most was the look on Owen's face. His mouth was slightly open, and he looked mesmerized by her. Once they reached the end, Ellis had to give him a nudge to wake him from his trance.

"I give you my heart, Owen. Take care of her."

"I will."

Henry then kissed her cheek and put her hand in his. She stepped up in front of him with a big smile.

"You look beautiful.

"Thank you. You look very handsome," Veronica said, trying not to cry.

After the vows, Ellis handed Owen the ring.

"It is beautiful," she whispered.

"It was your mother's," he replied.

Veronica looked over at her father, who smiled at her. A tear rolled down her face as she looked at her hand. Owen reached up and wiped the tear with his thumb. Everyone saw the loving gesture and began to think there were feelings between them.

That scared Ada. She started to feel threatened and needed to do something about it.

"I need the ribbon," said the Vicar.

Hannah stood up and gave him a blue ribbon. At that time, an altar boy brought over a box that held a ceremonial knife. Most people from England had never witnessed a binding ceremony, so that fascinated them, including Owen. The people from Scotland were pleased she showed respect for their heritage.

As their hands were being bonded, the vicar spoke. "May you both be blessed with the strength of heaven, the light of the sun, and the radiance of the moon. The splendor of fire. The speed of lightning. The swiftness of wind. the depth of the sea. The stability of earth, and the firmness of rock.

"I now pronounce you husband and wife. You may kiss your bride."

Owen leaned in and gave her a sweet, soft kiss. They parted and smiled at each other.

The crowd started clapping as Veronica and Owen turned toward the well-wishers. The longer Ada watched, the more she realized she had to do something to ensure she was still in control.

Once finished and on their way to the vestry, Veronica looked up at the balcony, and out of respect, the men bowed and the women curtsied. That's when she saw Lydia and Adrian. She was so glad they came, even though it was risky.

Lydia wiped away a tear, and Adrian pulled her close to him.

"I am so happy for her," she said.

"Me too."

As they signed the registry, everyone left the church and headed back to the castle for the wedding breakfast. Henry had arranged for a ball later that afternoon. Knowing the servants and town folks did not want to mingle with Englishmen, Veronica set up a party for them in town. So that was the first place they stopped after leaving the church.

When they entered the tavern, everyone stopped talking, surprised to see they were there.

Sean and Kieran walked up and shook Owen's hand and hugged Veronica.

"Where is Seinaid?" asked Veronica.

"Liam took her home. She hated not seeing you, but he is so worried about her condition, he gets overprotective," said Kieran.

"I understand," she replied.

Then a man stood up, getting everyone's attention.

"I want to say something to the newly married couple," he said in his thick accent as everyone grew quiet. "A thousand welcomes to you with your marriage. May you be healthy all of your days. May you be blessed with long life and peace. May you grow old with goodness and with riches." He then held up a cup of wine, and so did everyone else. "Saining," was said in unison.

Veronica put her hand on her chest as her heart grew with love for those people. She then walked over and took a cup of wine, and with the help of a man, she stood on the table.

Everyone grew quiet again.

"I would first like to say to Sean, Kieran, and Seinaid, who is not here because of the beautiful bairn she is having, thank you for being my charaid. And I am happy to call her husband, Lord Donaldson, mo charaid."

Everyone cheered and then quieted back down.

"What did she say?" Owen asked Sean.

"Charaid means friend."

Veronica continued to speak, holding up her cup. "To Scotland, akhom arched, and to all of you, lang yer lum reek. Slainte Mhath."

Everyone stood up and raised their cups. "SLAINTE MHATH!" and took a drink.

Sean leaned over. "She said to Scotland, I love you, and to everyone, long may your chimney smoke, cheers."

Owen looked confused. "Why would she wish a chimney to smoke?"

"It is a blessing," Sean said, laughing.

"Oh." Owen laughed with him. He then walked over to Veronica and helped her off the table.

"You are good at making people love you," he whispered. She blushed at the feel of his breath on her skin.

*Can I get you to love me?* she thought.

"We need to leave now," said Owen.

"Okay, let me say goodbye to Sean and Kieran."

After their goodbyes and all the well wishes, they were on their way to the castle.

"I liked the binding ceremony. It was nice to be a part of other people's customs. It makes me feel like one of them," said Owen as he looked at the small cut on his palm.

"I am glad you feel that way. I spent as much time as I could hear. My grandfather instilled a Scottish pride in Ellis and me."

"I saw that tonight when we were at the tavern. You spoke from the heart."

She took a deep breath. "Now, I need to pull out my English side."

Both stared at each other and started laughing.

"Yes, I guess you do."

For hours, they received congratulations and well wishes. Then, finally, everyone went to their rooms to change for the ball.

Lydia was waiting when Veronica entered. "Your wedding was beautiful."

"I could not have asked for anything better. It made me happy for you and Adrian to be here."

"I could not miss it."

"What are you going to do the rest of the evening?"

"I think I am going to the kitchen and devouring the rest of the wedding cakes. After all, you had ten different ones," Lydia said with a smile.

"While you do that, pick the one you want for your wedding."

"My wedding?" she said, surprised.

"Yes," Veronica said as she left smiling.

As Veronica walked down the stairs, she saw Ada standing by the doors leading to the ballroom, talking to some girls she had met a couple of times and did not like.

As she walked by, Ada turned to look at her. "Veronica."

"Ada," she replied and continued walking into the ballroom.

Ada was waiting to try to get a moment alone with Owen.

Little two-and-a-half-year-old John, whose mother worked at Veronica's home in London, was running, playing with the other servants' children. Not paying attention, he ran into Ada.

"I sowwy, miss," said John.

Ada was always cruel to servants, no matter the age, and was disgusted by being touched by him. Her temper flared, and she shoved him hard to the ground. "You filth, how dare you touch me," she hollered, scaring John so much, he started crying.

"ADA!" She looked over and saw Owen walking up, angry. He bent down and stood John up, checking to ensure he was okay. "You hurt?" he asked softly.

"No, sir," replied John, wiping his face with his sleeve.

"Is your mother around?"

"Yes, she in the ki'hen."

"Go to her and stay around the servants, okay?"

"Yes, sir." Owen patted him on the head, and he took off running to find his mother.

"Don't ever hurt a child again. I don't care if it is a servant's kid. Do you hear me?" Owen growled.

"I am sorry. I was just frustrated. He took me by surprise, and I lashed out. It will not happen again," she said, looking down, acting ashamed.

Owen walked on by and into the ball, looking for Veronica. He saw her standing with Hannah and Dinah and noticed how pretty she looked in her layered, yellow taffeta gown. They stopped talking as Owen walked up. He held out his hand to Veronica and dipped his head a little toward her.

"Would you care to dance?"

"Yes, I would," she replied with a smile.

A waltz was starting up, and Owen held her close. He looked down at her as they moved across the dance floor. "Are you happy?" He wasn't sure why he asked that. It just seemed important to him that she was happy.

"Yes, very." She smiled as she looked up at him. He couldn't look away, getting lost in her beautiful blue eyes.

For Veronica, the last four months had brought so many emotions. At first, she was afraid of it all being a cruel joke, but she changed after he kissed her. Unknowingly, she had opened her heart and let him in. There was no doubt she was in love with him. Heart-stopping, never going back, love.

As Ada stood in the corner watching them, the corner of her mouth rose. *Be happy now, because it won't last,* she thought as she left the room.

As the night ended, most of the guests had indulged in a little too much wine, including Owen and Ellis. Veronica went to her room to get ready for her wedding night. After changing, she wasn't sure if Owen would come to her room or if she was supposed to go to his. They never discussed that, so she put on her robe and decided to go to his.

After bathing, Owen realized he had drunk more than he intended to. He was drying off when he heard a knock. Wrapping the towel around himself, he answered the door, thinking it was Veronica.

But, instead, it surprised him that it was Ada standing there.

"What are you doing here?"

"I just cannot do this," she says as she walks past him.

Owen swings the door to close it as he follows Ada. "Cannot do what?"

"I was wrong, Owen. I thought I could handle you being married to someone else, but I am scared."

"You are scared." He sounded sarcastic. "I did not want to do this, remember? I had to marry Veronica because of your mother."

"I know, Owen. I know you were forced into doing this, but I watched you with her, and I am scared of losing your love." She started crying, knowing Owen always got soft and would do anything to stop her tears.

"Please, do not cry." He walked over and hugged her.

"Could you please be with me tonight? I know I should not ask this, but I must know you still love me."

"I cannot, Ada. This is my wedding night. How am I supposed to explain to Veronica not being with her?"

"You could tell her you had too much to drink, and you do not feel well. She would believe you."

"Ada. We agreed not to do this until after I am divorced."

"I know we did. If I have to, I will go and tell her everything. I cannot lose you. I love you more than the money, even if it means making my mother disown me and I lose everything."

He took a deep breath and looked at her tear-stained face. "Okay, I will try."

"My room is on the second floor. First door on the right," she said, then they kissed before she left the room.

While they were talking, neither one knew; the door didn't close all the way, and Veronica was standing outside, listening. She turned and walked back toward her room in a daze.

Once back, she stood in the center of her room, looking at everything inside. The four-poster bed, side tables, wardrobe, couch and chairs, the rugs on the floor. That is what money buys; they did it for money. He loved Ada; he did it for Ada.

She walked to the window and stared at nothing when she heard a knock at the door.

"Come in."

"Veronica?" said Owen as he walked inside.

"I am sorry, but I am not feeling well. I must have drunk too much. I am going to rest tonight." He was quiet as he waited for her to answer.

She didn't even turn around. "I understand," was all she said.

"I will see you tomorrow," he said before he left.

She spun around when she heard the door shut as if waking from a dream. "Please come back," she whispered as tears fell from her chin. "Please, do not go. Please, I beg you, come back." But the door never opened.

She slowly sank to the floor, wrapping her arms around her legs and burying her face between her knees. Wretched sobs tore from her as the pain engulfed her heart. The pain of being a fool. The pain of knowing the man she loved was spending the night in the arms of another woman.

Owen walked up to Ada's door and stopped. Through the fog of alcohol, something told him not to do it. Instead, he put his hands on the door frame and laid his head on the door, trying to clear his thoughts.

Thinking she heard something, Ada opened the door to find Owen stumbling. She reached out and grabbed him and pulled him inside.

In the hall, hidden in an alcove, little John was playing a hiding game with the other children. Seeing Owen being pulled into the room by Ada, he got scared, thinking his new master was being attacked, and ran to get help.

When John came running in, Lydia and Adrian were sitting in the servants' dining room.

"Unc Aidn, Unc Aidn, help new mater. The bad woman gwabbed him in her rum."

Adrian looked at Lydia. "What did he say?"

"He said the bad women grabbed the new master into her room." Lydia has been around John enough to understand his two-year-old language.

John shook his head yes.

"Who is the bad woman?" asked Adrian.

"That must be Ada. Amy told me about an incident that happened today. John, are you talking about the woman who pushed you down today?"

"Yes, she gwabbed him in her rum."

"Is he saying Owen is in Ada's room?" asked Adrian.

"John, go find your mother. We will look. Okay?" said Lydia.

John took off running to find his mother.

"Surely not," said Adrian.

"One way to find out," said Lydia as she got up.

They left the dining room and headed to Ada's room.

"You know which room is hers?"

"Yes, Veronica told me where everyone was staying so I could avoid that area," said Lydia as they went to the second floor. As they grew close, they started walking slowly and quietly. Once there, they pressed their ears to the door to listen. It wasn't hard to hear the moans coming from inside.

Looking at each other in shock, they walk a few feet away, not to be heard.

"Do you think it is Owen in there? Would he do this?" asked Adrian

"I would have once said no, but I do not know what to think. I am more worried about Veronica. Maybe we should go and check on her."

"Do you think she knows?" asked Adrian.

"Let us go see."

As they reached Veronica's room, they could hear crying. Lydia didn't knock. She just slowly opened the door to see her on the floor with her head between her knees. She walked to Veronica and kneeled down, lightly touching her shoulder.

"Veronica," she said in a low voice.

She looked up and reached out. Lydia wrapped her in her arms and held her as she cried. A tear fell from Lydia's eyes as she looked at Adrian. He turned his head away as he listened to her pain and became angry at Owen for doing that to her.

After a while, Veronica grew quiet, and her arms relaxed. She had fallen asleep from sheer exhaustion.

"Let us get her to bed," said Adrian as he gently removed her from Lydia's embrace and picked her up. Veronica stirred but did not wake. Lydia turned down the bedsheets, and Adrian laid her down softly.

"I will stay with her," Lydia said.

"So will I. She may need both of us. I will sleep on the couch and keep the fire going."

Lydia walked over to the trunk, pulled out a quilt and pillow, and put them on the couch for Adrian.

"Thank you, sweetheart."

"I cannot believe this is happening. Why would Owen do this to her?" asked Lydia.

Adrian wrapped his arms around her. "I do not know, but I have a feeling there is more going on that we do not know, and none of it will be good for her."

# CHAPTER FIFTEEN

It's not a shame to be deceived,
but it is to stay in the deception...

Olivia

The following day, Veronica woke up before sunrise. Her eyes hurt and felt swollen. She looked to her right and saw Lydia beside her, asleep. She was a little confused at first, but then everything came back.

Owen, Ada, her marriage, everything, and tears threatened to fall again.

She lay there a while, thinking about what to do. Should she tell her father? But she knew that meant Owen would suffer an unfortunate accident. Even though she was hurting, she didn't want him dead, but she needed time to think. The thought of seeing Owen and Ada right now made her nauseous.

She looked at Lydia, wondering why she was there. Then, hearing a sound by the fire, Veronica looked and saw a leg extending out. That must be Adrian. Lately, when one saw Lydia, Adrian was not far behind. He must care for her, maybe even love her.

*For her sake, I hope he does,* thought Veronica. She reached over and touched Lydia lightly. "Lydia, wake up."

Lydia stirred and slowly opened her eyes, seeing Veronica staring at her.

"Why did you come here last night? How did you know?"

Lydia was quiet, not wanting to tell her what she and Adrian heard at Ada's door.

"You can tell me."

"Little John saw Owen at Ada's door."

"Little John?"

"Yes. He must have been hiding. He came running into the dining room, asking Adrian to save the new master from the bad woman."

Veronica couldn't help but smile, thinking about little John. "Why did he think Owen needed saving?"

"He said Ada grabbed Owen and pulled him into her room. He must think that since he is afraid of her."

"Why is he afraid of her?"

"I will tell you about that later. Right now, you need to think about what you will do." Veronica stayed quiet. "Are you okay?" asked Lydia.

"No, I am not. I feel like my heart is dying. God help me, Lydia, but I still love him." Tears rolled down the side of her face. Lydia reached over and wiped her face. "I need to leave. I do not think I can handle seeing them today," she said, taking a deep breath, trying to stop the tears.

"Okay, then we leave." Lydia pushed back the covers and rose, and so did Veronica.

Walking over to Adrian, Lydia kneeled and put her hand on his shoulder. "Love, wake up," she said. Lydia looked up and saw Veronica standing there watching. "I am sorry."

"No, do not ever hide your love. You must cherish it. Always."

Lydia smiled and put her hand on the side of Adrian's face. "Love, wake up."

He opened his eyes and smiled as he looked at Lydia. "Morning," he said, stretching.

"You need to get up. Veronica wants to leave."

Remembering last night, he sat up and looked around to see Veronica standing there.

"Sorry you had to sleep on that uncomfortable couch," Veronica said, giving him a slight smile.

"It was not that bad. So, you want to leave?"

"Yes, I do. I need time away to think."

Adrian got up and stretched. "Okay, I am going to go change and pack a bag. Then I will prepare a carriage and drive back."

"You want to drive the carriage?" asked Lydia.

"The fewer people that know, the better." He then looked at Veronica. "What are you going to tell everyone?"

"I do not know."

"We could say something came up, and we had to return to London," said Lydia.

"I will leave Owen a letter telling him to meet me in four days at my home. That should give me enough time to come up with something. My head hurts already just thinking about it."

"I am going to go and let you two get ready," said Adrian. He kissed Lydia on the forehead, walked to Veronica, and hugged her. "Everything will be okay. Eventually," he said, then left the room.

"What will everyone think of me leaving without him?"

"Does it matter? If people find out where he is, there is nothing that can save them. We need to bring Hannah with us. She was always good at solving things," said Lydia.

"Yes, once we are finished, go wake her up. Please do not tell her why. Just say it is important. I would not put it past her to drag Ada out in front of everyone and have her flogged."

Lydia could not help but laugh. "I would love to see that."

"So would I."

Lydia helped Veronica get dressed and pack a few things for the journey. She then went to her room and did the same before going to wake up Hannah. She did not knock to avoid attracting attention.

Inside, she walked up and lightly touched her shoulder. "Hannah, wake up."

Hannah opens her eyes and saw a figure standing over her. She screamed, causing Lydia to scream.

"Hannah, it is me, Lydia. You scared me."

"Lydia?" Once Hannah calmed down, she got mad. "Scared you? I almost died from fright. Why did you not light a lamp?"

"Sorry, did not think about it," Lydia said as she walked over to the fireplace and lit a stick to start lighting candles.

"Why are you here? It is not even daylight."

"Veronica needs help. You need to get dressed and pack a bag. We are heading back to London."

"What happened to Veronica?"

"She will tell you in the carriage. We need to hurry. I will help you get ready."

"I will need to leave a letter for my parents."

Once Hannah was ready to leave, she left a letter on her pillow for the maid to give to her parents.

When Veronica was ready to leave the castle, she gave Ailbert two letters—one for Owen and the other for Ellen.

"Please wait until I leave before you give those out."

Ailbert looked at Veronica and knew something was wrong. "Miss Veronica, is everything all right?"

"Yes," is all she said as she left.

When Hannah and Lydia made their way outside, they saw Adrian waiting beside the carriage. Once they stepped up, he opened the door, and they saw Veronica inside.

Owen slowly opened his eyes but closed them as the light coming through the windows made his head hurt even worse.

*Oh, I drank too much last night,* he thought.

As he lay there, he tried to remember everything that had happened. Then, everything started returning: the wedding, the party at the tavern, the castle celebration, and dancing with Veronica. Then he remembered Ada coming to his room and him going to Veronica.

*Please, let me have stayed with Veronica,* he thought.

Looking over, he saw Ada lying beside him, asleep.

"Oh, god, what have I done?" He whispered. He sat up, swung his legs over the side, and grabbed his head as pain shot through his temple. Ada stirred as Owen got up and started getting dressed.

She opened her eyes and smiled. "Leaving so soon?" she asked, stretching.

Owen was quiet as he dressed. Once finished, he turned to look at Ada. "I married Veronica because I had no choice, but what happened last night is all on me. I wanted to at least walk away with some self-respect and dignity. I do not even have that anymore."

"It is okay. She will never know."

"But I know. I cheated on my wife on my wedding day. My God, Ada, what is enough?" He ran his hands through his hair. "I cannot talk to you right now. I need to go and be alone for a while." He turned and walked towards the door.

"Are you angry with me?" Ada asked.

"No, I am angry with myself." He then left the room.

Ada sat in bed, smiling. Being able to take away Veronica's wedding night made her so happy, and that was only the start of her quest to destroy Veronica's life.

*The girl that has everything cannot even keep a husband.*

After Owen returned to his room, he sat in the bath for quite a while, thinking about how far he had fallen. He decided to go to Veronica and try to make it up to her without revealing what he had done.

Once dressed, he went downstairs to breakfast, thinking he would find her there. At the bottom of the stairs, he found Ailbert waiting. As he walked up, he handed Owen a letter. Confused, he opened it.

"She left?"

"Yes, sir, before the sun was up. She and Miss Hannah."

"Did she say why?"

"No, sir, but if I may say, she did not look well."

"What do you mean?"

"She looked pale and like she had been crying." Ailbert watched closely to see his reaction.

Owen grew pale. *Does she know?* he thought. "Did any of her guards go with her?"

"I informed Aaron and Ian. They left right after."

"Have a horse readied for me." He turned back toward the stairs to go pack, then stopped. "Don't tell anyone about this, please."

"Of course, my lord."

Owen then proceeded up the stairs with Ailbert watching. *I do not know what you did, but you will pay dearly,* he thought as he walked into the great hall where everyone was eating breakfast.

Ailbert walked toward the head of the table where Henry sat, Ellis to his right and Ellen to his left. "Pardon, my lord. I have a letter for Lady

Ellen." He then leaned down and handed the letter to her. Henry and Ellis watched, wondering who would be sending Ellen a letter.

"She left for London."

"Who?" asked Henry.

"Veronica, she left this morning for London."

"I thought they were going to stay here for a few days?" said Ellis.

"Owen go with her?" asked Henry.

"It does not say."

"Sir, Lord Pierce is also headed for London." Leaving out the part where they didn't go together. Whatever happened, Ailbert had confidence Veronica could handle it.

"Well, once the guests leave, we will also head back," said Henry.

Ellen had a bad feeling about this. It was not like Veronica to just leave like that. Especially with so many guests, but she would have to wait until she returned to find out why.

During that time, Veronica had finished telling Hannah everything that had transpired the night prior. She sat there, unable to say a word. Hannah looked between Lydia and Veronica several times, trying to absorb the fact that Owen had slept with Ada instead of his wife.

"I never pictured Owen as a dirty beau. Are you sure? I mean, are you sure he went there, and they had sex?" asked Hannah.

"Lydia and Adrian went to her bedroom to make sure," said Veronica, taking Lydia by surprise.

"How did you know?" asked Hannah, looking at Lydia.

Once Lydia was done telling Hannah how she and Adrian knew about Owen, she couldn't think of anything to say.

Veronica looked out at the scenery but didn't see it as her mind relived last night. She did not cry anymore.

Hannah and Lydia looked at each other with worried expressions.

"Veronica, what are you going to do?" asked Hannah.

"I have no idea," she replied, not turning away from the window.

"Do you think Owen will come looking for you, or will he just wait at your home?" Hannah asked.

"I do not know. That is why I asked Adrian to go a different way back."

For the next two days, they tried to get Veronica to talk about how she felt. They could see she was shutting down. All she would do was respond with one word. Then, on the final day before reaching London, Hannah had a question that would change everything for her.

"Veronica?" Hannah said, looking at her blank expression. "What did you want besides a husband who cared about you from this marriage? Since we now know Owen had a different plan, that is not an option. I know you do not want to talk about it, but you need to decide what you want out of this. It is not right for you to walk away with nothing."

Veronica looked at Hannah and then down at the floor as if in deep thought. The next thing they knew, she raised her head with a slight smile on her face. "I know what I want and how to make sure Owen gives it to me."

After dropping off Hannah, Veronica had one more place to go to in London before heading home—St. Martin's church.

"Wait here, please. I will not be long," said Veronica as she walked up the stairs to the church.

Inside, she sat up front and stared at the cross as she released the tears she had been holding in.

"I have tried so hard to be a good person. I had turned the other cheek when people were horrible to me. I have tried to help as many people as I could, even risking my own life. I do not understand what I could have done to deserve this. Am I not worthy of love? I know

I am not supposed to question and have faith, but it is hard when it hurts so bad."

She stayed quiet for a moment, then took a deep breath and wiped her face.

"Forgive me for my sins, dear God, and if it be your will, let Owen agree to my offer. I am not asking for revenge or any ill will against those who have hurt me. That is left to you. Thank you for all I have, and please protect those I love. I pray for strength to do what I need to do."

She then stood up and left, ready to face Owen.

When Owen reached the house on Broad's Street, a stable boy let him in because the rest of the servants were still in Scotland. Seeing Veronica had not made it yet, he decided to get the house in order. So, he had the stable boy start a fire in the dayroom while he removed the furniture's coverings.

"Is there something to eat?" Owen asked.

"There is some meat and cheese. Rachel from next door has made sure I have had plenty to eat while everyone is gone."

"Good, show me the kitchen." Owen wanted to have something for Veronica when she arrived. He knew she should be there anytime, and he was nervous, wondering why she had left. After preparing the food tray, he went into the dayroom and opened the curtains, letting the light brighten the gloomy atmosphere. It wasn't long before he heard voices in the hall.

As he opened the door, he saw a figure walking up the stairs. *That must be her lady's maid,* he thought as he watched the woman walk away. He had a strange feeling that the maid looked familiar. He shrugged the feeling off, thinking he must have seen her already and just didn't remember.

"Owen."

He turned around and saw Veronica standing there, staring at him. She had a sad look, and that made him nervous.

"How was the ride back?" he asked, wanting to break the awkward feeling he had.

"Long," was all she said as she entered the dayroom. "Please, sit. We have some things to discuss," Veronica said as she sat on the couch.

Owen sat in the chair, facing her, getting more nervous as he noticed how withdrawn she was. "What is going on? Why did you leave without telling me?"

She took a deep breath and looked at him. "I needed some time to think about what to do."

"About what?"

"Well, let me start with what I know. I know you married me because of Agnes. I know you intend to divorce me so you can be with Ada. I also know you spent our wedding night in Ada's bed." She watched as his face grew pale as she talked. "I need you to be honest with me now. It will help me to determine my next decision."

"How did you find out?" he asked as he lowered his head in shame.

"I went to your room thinking it was supposed to be me with you after we married. How stupid was that? Hearing you and Ada talking did not seem real, but then you came to my room and made it all true. After that, I could not stand the thought of seeing you two the next day, so I left."

"I am so sorry," he said as he closed his eyes.

"I do not want your apology. I want the truth. All of it, please. I think I deserve that."

He looked at Veronica and noticed her expression was blank. She sat there, not moving, just staring at him, waiting. "Agnes threatened to out my family's situation. She did not leave me any choice in the matter."

"How were you going to divorce me without any consequences?"

"Let me first say I would not allow them to hurt you. I was going to ask for a divorce."

"What were they planning?" asked Veronica with an uneasy feeling.

"Agnes was going to have you compromised." He couldn't look at her while he spoke.

Veronica closed her eyes, not surprised. That sounded like something Agnes would do. "Does Dinah know?"

Owen's head snapped up. "She did not know until right before the wedding. That is why my mother sent her to our aunts. She wanted me to call it off, but it was too late."

Veronica's heart sank. She was so hoping Dinah hadn't known.

"Please, don't be mad at her. She was trapped between you and me."

They grew quiet and sat there for a few minutes before Owen got the courage to ask what was next.

"What do we do now?"

"I have a proposition for you. I will give you my dowry and divorce on one condition."

"What is it?"

"A child."

"A child?" He was so confused.

"Yes, I want a child. Since I cannot have a marriage with love, I want a child."

Owen was speechless. That was the last thing he expected. "You want a child with me?"

"Yes, even though I know you do not care for me, you are still my husband, and I want a child. I want someone I can love and who will love me back."

Guilt hit him hard, and regret wrapped around his heart as he realized what he had done to her heart. "All right."

"We need to discuss a few things before you agree."

"What things?"

"First, you will not disrespect me again as you did at the castle. You will stay away from Ada until after the divorce."

"That will not happen again."

"Second, if I have a boy, he will inherit your title and everything that goes with it."

"If you have a boy, he will be my oldest and inherit my title."

"Before you agree, you will need to discuss this with your family, especially Ada. Because this will mean they inherit nothing if you have children with her."

"Okay, I will discuss this with them, but I see no problem."

"Oh, but there will be. When Ada disagrees, and she will, tell her if everyone is okay with this, I will give you this house."

"This house? Where will you live?"

"Once the baby is old enough to travel, I will move to Blackthorn permanently."

"You will take my child away from me?"

"I will never keep the baby away from its father. Even though your actions are despicable, I believe you would be a good father."

"Thank you," said Owen as he relaxed.

"Now, you need to go and talk to your family," said Veronica as she stood.

"Oh, um, my father does not know about this. So please do not say anything in the future when you are around my family."

"You do not have to worry. I will not say anything to him."

"Thank you," he said as he stood and left.

Once Owen was gone, Veronica sat back down, covered her face with her hands, and cried.

When Owen got home, he went to his room to finish packing his things but found they were all ready to go.

*Edgar is such a good valet,* thought Owen.

As he lay down to rest, he went over everything he and Veronica discussed. She had seemed calm. She should have been angry and maybe even a little violent. God knows she could have hurt him if she had wanted to, but she didn't. He could tell she had been crying, which made his heart heavy. He didn't understand why her crying bothered him so much, but he would make it up to her in any way he could. If that meant a baby, then that was what he would give her, no matter if everyone agreed or not.

Hopefully, his family will return quickly, and he would talk to his mother. Dinah would need to be involved in the conversation since Veronica knew everything.

Once Veronica stopped crying, she went to her room where Lydia and Adrian were waiting.

"How did it go?" asked Lydia as Veronica joined them by the fireplace.

"He went to his parent's house to wait for their return. His father does not know what his family was planning."

"Really?" replied Lydia.

"I think his mother and Agnes had him do this. Owen said Dinah found out right before the wedding."

"Why did she not say anything?"

"She was probably protecting her family. I just do not know how to feel about that. I want to understand, but I cannot right now."

"You just need time. Then, after a while, when things have settled between you and Owen, you can figure out what to do about Dinah," said Adrian.

"You truly are brilliant, Adrian. It was my good fortune to have come across you," said Veronica.

"The fortune was mine. You saved me and gave me the life I always wanted." He looked at Lydia.

Veronica smiled as she watched Adrian and Lydia stare at each other, evidently in love. "Well, I probably have at least one more day before everyone returns from Scotland. One more day before I have to act like everything is okay."

"Are you going to be able to do this? Pretend everything is okay between you and Owen?" asked Lydia.

"When I think about holding a small bundle in my arms…" Veronica said with a smile. "Then I will return to my home in Scotland and live peacefully. For that, I can."

"Do you think Ada will be compliant and not cause any problems?" asked Lydia.

"No, I do not. But she does not know that I am no longer playing nice. So, if Ada wants to cause trouble, that is what she will get."

Lydia knew things were not going to be easy. If anyone knew how horrible Ada could be, it was her.

"Lydia. I can tell you are worried. I have been thinking, and I am ready for Ada."

"Do not hold back because she will not."

Owen woke the following day as his valet was laying out his clothes.

"Good morning, Edgar."

"Good morning, my Lord. Breakfast is ready."

After dressing, he went to the dining room. Not long after he finished eating, he heard a noise at the front door. Walking out of the dining room, he saw his mother and sister removing their cloaks.

"Where is Father?"

"Owen, what are you doing here?" asked Ann.

"Getting the rest of my belongings. Where is Father?"

"He had some business he needed to tend to."

"Good, we need to talk," he said as he walked past them into the dayroom.

"What is going on? Why did you and Veronica leave so quickly without saying anything to anybody?" asked Dinah.

"That is what I need to talk to you both about. Veronica knows everything."

"What do you mean everything?" asked Ann.

"I did something horrible, and please do not hate me," he said, looking at Dinah.

"What did you do?"

"The night of our wedding, Ada came to my room. She was upset and was worried that I would stop loving her." He stopped talking and looked down.

"And?" asked Ann.

"We were discussing things, and Veronica was at the door, listening. She heard enough to figure out what our plans were."

"What did Veronica say?" asked Dinah, worried about her friend.

"She left the next morning. So, I did not know until I got a letter from her that she was on her way back to London, and I was to meet her at her home yesterday."

"Wait, she did not say anything and just left the following day. How did you not know? Where were you, Owen?" asked Dinah.

"I was with Ada," he said in a low voice.

"Dear god, please tell me you did not spend your wedding night with Ada and not Veronica? How could you do something so disgusting?" yelled Dinah.

"I had too much to drink and was not thinking clearly. I regret it more than you know."

"Poor Veronica, she must be devastated."

"You have talked to her since you have been back?" asked Ann.

"Yes, I talked to her yesterday, and she has offered a solution. I can have her dowry, and she will take the blame for the divorce in exchange for a child."

Everyone was quiet as they thought about what Owen had just said, but they heard a noise at the door before anyone could speak. They all turned to look, and Owen saw his father standing there in a rage.

Unknown to everyone, Callum had returned to retrieve some paperwork he had forgotten.

"What have you done?" he said as he looked at his family.

Callum walked up to Owen and slapped him across the face. Ann and Dinah sat in shock, not having ever seen Callum so angry.

"How could you do such a disgusting thing?"

"Callum, let me explain," said Ann trying to calm him down.

"Explain? How will you explain that my family has used a sweet girl for her money to ruin her with a divorce?" Callum yelled as he ran his hands through his hair. Owen sat with his head down, not saying a word. He knew there was nothing he could say to make what he had done okay in his father's eyes. "I thought you were better than this, Owen."

Still, Owen said nothing.

"He had no choice. Agnes threatened to tell everyone about our situation if Owen did not marry Veronica."

"Agnes? Of course, Agnes. And you bow down to and obey everything she says," said Callum sarcastically. He walked over to the fireplace and put his hands on the mantle with his head lowered. "What did Veronica say?" Callum asked as he pushed himself back up straight.

Owen raised his head as he looked at his father. "She offered to give me the money and a divorce in exchange for a baby."

"A baby?"

"Yes, she wants to have a baby. Something she can love is what she said. So, we are to pretend to be a normal married couple until after the baby is born. Then she will move to Scotland with the child."

"You will give her whatever she asks for because you do not have any idea what could happen if Henry finds out the truth."

"I know he is a dangerous man," said Owen.

"No, son, you do not know. The friend loaning us money is Henry. He does not have to do anything but call in his markers, and we are living on the streets."

Everyone froze, not knowing what to say.

"Why did you not tell us?" asked Ann.

"I did not think I had to protect my family from my family." He then looks at Dinah as if he had just noticed her there. "And you, this is what was wrong with you in the carriage? You hid this from me."

"I did not know what to do. I had just found out."

"I could have done something. She was your friend."

Dinah lowered her head, knowing she should have told him.

He looked at Ann and said nothing, just stared. Finally, he walked out of the room, not looking back. Ann followed him out the door while Owen and Dinah stayed seated.

"Do you think he will ever forgive us?" asked Dinah.

"He might you but not me," he says as he looks at his sister.

"Now I know why Veronica left without talking to me. She knew and probably thought I was in on the plan."

"I told her you did not find out until right before the wedding."

"It does not matter. I still kept quiet, which was a betrayal."

"I have ruined so much. How did I get here?"

She wanted to tell him it was because he was an idiot for loving Ada, but when she saw a tear fall from his face, she felt sorry for him and didn't want to make it worse.

"I should get going. Veronica wanted me to talk to Ada before I gave her an answer," said Owen as he stood.

"Why?"

"Because if she has a boy, he will inherit my title. Which means any children I have with Ada will get very little."

Owen left, leaving Dinah there, thinking about what it would mean for Ada if Veronica had a boy.

She smiled. "Excellent, Veronica," whispered Dinah.

Ada hated Veronica, and if her child took anything away from Ada, she would retaliate one way or another. Veronica just set Ada up to show her true self. Dinah decided to wait and see what would happen. If there was any way to help, she would be ready.

Ann followed Callum into his office.

"Please, try to understand. We had no choice," she said, desperately wanting him not to be angry.

Callum stopped and turned around to face her.

"Do you remember how those women treated you when you first entered society? They were horrible to you, especially Agnes. Well, congratulations, you are now one of them." He then picked up some papers and left her in his office.

She sank into one of the chairs as tears fall from her eyes. Ann never thought she would become so heartless as the women of the ton, but she had, and now she might have lost her husband's respect and love.

Owen sent a message to Ada and waited in the carriage for her to arrive. When Ada opened the door, she found him with his head down and eyes closed. Then, hearing a noise, he raised his head but did not smile. Ada knew something was wrong.

Sitting next to him, she took his hand. "What is wrong, my love?"

"They all know. My Father, Veronica, they know everything," he said in a low voice.

"How?" Ada was worried that their plan had been ruined and the money gone.

"The night at the castle when you came to my room, Veronica was outside the door, listening. She heard everything and also that I spent the night with you."

Ada's face grew pale. She feared what Veronica would do. "Is that why you left the following day? She demanded you go with her?"

"Veronica left before we were even up. I went after I received a letter from her letting me know she was headed back to London. When we talked yesterday, she was very calm and even offered me a compromise."

"A compromise?"

"She will hold to the marriage contract and will give me a divorce in exchange for a child."

"A child? That is all?"

"She wants a child to love, but we must act like everything is okay between us until the divorce. That means I cannot be with you or do anything that would disrespect her."

"Okay, that does not sound too bad," said Ada, relaxing.

"There is something else. If she has a boy, he will inherit my title and everything that comes with it."

"What? No, I am afraid I have to disagree with that. Our children will not have anything. She does not get to take that away from mine."

"If everyone agrees, she will include her Broad's Street house." He watched Ada closely to see her reaction.

Ada was stunned for a second. "She will give you her home if everyone agrees to her terms?"

"Yes."

Ada was quiet as she thought about how living in that colossal townhouse would feel. She couldn't believe it. Even knowing that she could afford their own enormous house with the money from Veronica's dowry, she wanted that one. Her jealousy of Veronica had consumed her, and any rational thought was long gone.

"What do you think we should do? Do you want to agree with her?" Ada knew if she left it to Owen, he would give anything to Veronica. His conscience would make him. So, she could blame it on him.

Owen saw the change in her but didn't want to admit it, so he decided. "Yes, I am going to agree to her request. So, this will be the last time we are alone together until the divorce is final."

Ada wraps her arms around him and lays her head on his chest. "Just do not forget me."

"I could never forget you. I love you."

"I love you too."

# CHAPTER SIXTEEN

Respect was invented to
cover the empty place
where love should be

Leo Tolstoy

As Owen sat in the carriage on his way back to Veronica's, his mind was reliving the confrontation with his father. Tears welled up as he realized he had lost so much because of his actions—especially his father's respect. The only way to try and repair the damage he had done was to do what he could for Veronica. Giving her a child and acting as a good husband while they were married was the only way to right his wrong, and that was what he would do.

Arriving back, Owen was met at the door by the butler.

"Good afternoon, my Lord. I am Elliot."

"Nice to meet you. Is Veronica around?"

"I believe she is in the library."

"Could you direct me there? I am afraid I do not know my way around yet."

"Of course, this way." Elliot walked Owen down the hall to the door on the right. "This is it, my Lord."

"Thank you," said Owen as he opened and walked in.

He found Veronica in the back, sitting on the window seat, reading. She wore a yellow day dress, and her hair was down and flowing over her shoulders. She looked pretty sitting there with the sun shining in on her.

"Am I disturbing you?" Owen said, leaning against a bookshelf.

"No," she said as she shut the book she was reading.

He walked over and sat beside her.

"Do you have an answer for me?" she asked.

"The answer is yes."

Veronica smiled but noticed Owen seemed sad. "What is wrong? Do you not want to agree?"

"My father knows what I have done."

"How did he find out?"

"He overheard me talking to my mother."

"What did he say?"

"Let us just say I have much to make up for." He never looked up while talking.

Veronica reached out and grabbed his hand. "Your father loves you. He will get over it once he sees his grandchild."

"I did not think of that. My father has always wanted a house full of kids."

"See? Everything will work out," she said with a smile.

"How do you do that?"

"Do what?" Veronica asked, confused.

"You just found out the truth about me, yet you are still trying to make me feel better."

"I do not have any ill will towards you. It is not hard to understand that you want to protect your family. I wish you had been upfront with me."

"You are a good person, Veronica." He stood up and stretched. "It has been a long stressful day. I am going to go to my room and rest before supper." He walked to the door but stopped and turned back. "Do you mind telling me where my room is?"

Veronica smiled and got up. "I will show you."

They continued to talk as they left the library.

Later that evening, Veronica was headed down the stairs when she saw Elliot opening the door, and a man entered carrying a couple of bags. She walked up, and the man bowed. "I apologize, my Lady, for coming through the front, but I am unfamiliar with your home."

"And you are?" asked Veronica.

"I am Edgar. Lord Pierce's valet."

"Oh, of course. Elliot, show him to his room. Then, Edgar, after you have settled in, make sure Owen is up. Supper will be ready shortly."

"Yes. my lady."

"Thank you." She then turned and went to the kitchen to see if she could help. She walked into the kitchen, where most of the servants were eating. "Hello, everyone," she said.

"Hello, my lady," everyone replied.

"I was so glad most of you were able to come to my wedding," she said as she walked up to the stove to see what was cooking.

"Your wedding was beautiful," said Amy as she stirred one of the pots.

"Thank you. When will supper be ready?"

"It will be ready very soon."

"Great. I am gut-founded," said Veronica as she left the kitchen.

After Edgar settled in his room, surprised at how big his room was for a servant, he went to get Owen ready for supper. He knocked lightly and then entered, finding Owen still asleep. Edgar walked to the wardrobe to remove his evening wear, noticing the expensive furniture, then looked around at the blue embossed wallpaper, large thick rugs on the floor, and the beautiful blue duvet on the huge four-post bed. People hadn't exaggerated about how wealthy Lady Veronica was.

Owen woke to see Edgar preparing his clothes for the evening.

"Good evening, my lord. Supper will be ready shortly."

"Thank you, Edgar. How are your accommodations here?"

"Excellent, my lord."

"Good," said Owen as he changed his clothes.

Once Veronica was finished, she left her room ready for her first supper with Owen as husband and wife. Sadness washed over her as she wished it was a real marriage, not a temporary situation. Reaching the stairs, she saw Owen waiting at the bottom. She took a deep breath and smiled. She thought she might as well enjoy it while it lasted.

Making it to the bottom, Owen held out his arm. "May I escort you to dinner, my lady?"

"You certainly may," Veronica said as she wrapped her arm in his.

The rest of the evening, they talked about different things and even laughed at times. Once finished, they were getting up to leave when Owen took Veronica's hand and led her to the sitting room.

"I thought you might want a drink to relax."

"Yes, I would," she said as she walked over and sat down.

Owen poured two glasses of bourbon and walked over, handing her one before sitting across from her. They both are quiet while slowly drinking.

"Are you nervous about being with me?" asked Owen.

"Yes and no. It being my first time makes me nervous, but not being with you," she said with a smile.

Owen smiled, finished his drink, and stood. "I am going to my room and get a bath. Do I come to your room when I am finished?"

"No, I will come to yours," she said as she stood, and they both left, heading to their rooms.

After bathing, Veronica put on her nightgown and robe.

"I expect you to tell me everything," said Lydia.

"You know, you have a man in your life if you want to know," said Veronica, causing Lydia to blush.

"You need to get going before he thinks you have changed your mind," said Lydia. She pushed Veronica towards the door.

"Why do I keep you around?" asked Veronica.

"Because you love me. Now go make us a baby," she said as she pushed Veronica out the door and shut it before she could say a word.

"Us?" Veronica said, looking back at the door.

On the way to Owen's room, she tried to remember everything Angelique and Audrey had told her. She closed her eyes and breathed deeply when she reached his room.

*You are not a coward,* she thought as she knocked.

It didn't take a second for Owen to open the door, standing in a robe with a towel around his neck.

"Come in. I just finished bathing. Make yourself comfortable while I finish drying my hair." He turned and walked into the adjourning room.

Once finished, he walked back into the bedroom, finding Veronica sitting in the center of his bed. He walked over and stood beside the bed, staring at her. Veronica slowly crawled toward him, never breaking eye contact. Watching her come toward him with her hair falling beside her set his body on fire.

She sat before him and slowly started untying the belt to his robe. Once untied, she slowly ran her hands inside along his shoulders, pushing it off. He watched her eyes as she slowly moved her hands across his chest, exploring every detail. Making her way down, she finally looked at the part that separated a man from a woman.

Angelique was right. Those statues are way wrong about the size.

She wrapped her hand around his member. He sucked in a breath and closed his eyes as she ran her thumb over the top, feeling how silky and smooth it was. She leaned down and licked him, causing a moan to escape his throat. Using her hand, stroked him as she took the head in her mouth. He grabbed the bedpost to steady himself with one hand as he grabbed her shoulder with the other and pulled up, surprising her.

"Did I do something wrong?"

"No, lord no. It felt good, too good. I would not be able to control myself and take you too rough. It is your first time. I want to go slow."

She smiled at him as he leaned down and kissed her softly at first, then he used his tongue to open her mouth. She gasped as his tongue invaded her mouth. Slowly, he lay her back while never breaking the kiss. He ran her hand up her thigh, bringing her gown up, breaking the kiss to remove it altogether, leaving her bare for his view.

"You are beautiful," he said as his hands roamed from her breast down to her tiny waist. Everywhere he touched gave her a tingling sensation.

He took one of her breasts into his mouth as he massaged the other. She was completely unprepared for all the pleasure coursing through her. Moving his hands down her body, she was unaware of what he was doing until she felt him stroking between her legs. A tightness started building, and she started moving with his fingers.

"Owen," she whispered as her release hit her hard. Then, before her head had cleared from the euphoria, Owen positioned himself between her legs and made one swift thrust.

The pain quickly replaced her pleasure.

He stayed still to give her body time to adjust. "Breath, Veronica."

Once she relaxed a little, he started moving slowly. Knowing she was in pain, he didn't hold back as his release came, and he emptied himself inside her. After pulling out, Veronica let out a sigh of relief.

"I promise it will not hurt like that the next time." He lay beside her and reached over, pushing the sweat-soaked hair from her face.

"It was not' that bad at first," she said, pulling her legs together and up as she tried to roll on her side.

"Wait a minute. Let me get you a rag."

Owen got up and went into the washroom. While he was gone, she found her gown on the floor and moved slowly, trying to make her legs work. Not long after, he came back with a couple of wet rags. He handed one to her.

"Use this one to clean yourself up."

"Could you turn around?"

"Seriously? I think after tonight, you should not' be shy around me."

"Still," she said, looking away, blushing.

"Okay," he said, smiling as he turned around.

After she finished, she set the rag on the side table. "I am finished," she said, and he turned back around.

"Here, hold this one between your legs. The coolness will help."

She took the rag and placed it under her gown. She closed her eyes and visibly relaxed.

Owen smiled as he walked to the other side and lay down, pulling the covers up. "Lay down and get some sleep. Tomorrow you will be sour but better than how you feel right now."

She lay back and relaxed.

"Can I ask you something?" Owen asked.

"Sure."

"How did you know how to do what you did to me?"

Veronica was quiet, thinking about how to answer. "I asked some friends."

His head shot up from the bed. "My sister?"

Veronica laughed. "No, some older friends."

Owen rested his head back down, relieved. "Goodnight," he said, leaning over and kissing her forehead.

"Goodnight," she replied.

Owen didn't take long to fall into a deep sleep while Veronica lay awake, waiting for an opportunity to leave. She got up slowly, partly because she was sore but mainly because she didn't want to wake him up. She knew she needed to keep some distance between them. It would make the final separation easier. So, she decided not to ever spend the entire night with him.

The following day, Owen woke up and felt for Veronica but found an empty bed. She must have already gone for breakfast. Once bathed and dressed, he found her reading the paper in the dining room.

"Good morning," he said as he went to the bar and grabbed a plate.

"Good morning," she replied as she set the paper down.

After he filled his plate, he sat beside her.

"No, you sit there," she said, pointing to the head of the table.

Owen got up and moved.

"Happy?"

"Yes. Even though our situation is temporary, you are still the head of this household," she said, smiling.

"You got up early. Feeling better?"

"Yes, feeling good this morning."

"Good. What are your plans today?" Owen asked.

"I need to check on the orphanage and ensure they have enough supplies. Then, this afternoon, I will need to go over everything with you about the properties you will be handling for me until the divorce," Veronica said as she ate a piece of bacon.

Across town at White's gentlemen's club, Ada stood in front of a window in nothing but her shift.

"Come back to bed." She turned and looked at the man lying in bed with nothing on but a sheet. Jeremy Hightower was a handsome man with brown hair, brown eyes, and a nice, muscular body. He had tried to court Ada, but he was only a baron, and her mother wanted more.

"Jeremy, I need you to do something for me," she said as she walked toward the bed. She sat down beside him and started rubbing his leg.

"What?" he asked, smiling.

"I need you to compromise Veronica Aldridge."

"You are not serious."

"Yes, I am quite serious."

"Look, I know you are probably angry that Owen married her, but this is ridiculous."

"See, that is where you are wrong. Once Owen gets her money, they will divorce. My mother devised a plan, and Owen's family's financial situation is in dire straits. Well, let us just say it did not take much to convince his mother to force Owen to comply."

"You are saying this whole thing was a farce from the beginning?"

"Yes, at first, the plan was to compromise her so Owen could divorce her without taking the blame."

"I would never have thought Mr. Prim and Proper would do something so distasteful," Jeremy said, smiling.

"But she found out and made a counteroffer."

"Counteroffer?"

"Yes, Veronica would allow him to have her dowry and divorce in exchange for a child."

"A child?" Jeremy asked, surprised.

"If Owen gives her a child, she will walk away," said Ada, as she started moving higher up his leg.

"So, what is the problem?"

"If it is a boy, he will inherit Owen's title and everything, and my children will get nothing. I cannot have that," she snarled.

Jeremy sat up against the headboard.

"But, if someone else has sex with her, the child's paternity is questioned, and it will get nothing," she said with a smile.

Jeremy gets up and grabs his clothes.

"NO. Bloody hell, no. Do you have any idea what would happen to anyone who hurt Henry Aldridge's children, especially his daughter?"

"Yes, yes, I heard the rumors about him," she said, rolling her eyes.

"No, they are not rumors. He would kill them, Ada." He quickly put on his clothes.

"I never pictured you as a coward," said Ada, angry that he wouldn't help her.

"I am not stupid, and I want nothing to do with you. So do not contact me anymore," Jeremy said as he stormed out the door, leaving Ada fuming.

Across the room, a panel just big enough for someone to look through slowly closed. Seconds later, a gentleman left the adjoining room. He walked to the desk where an employee was working.

"I need to send a note."

"Yes, sir." The employee turned and hollered at a boy standing in the corner.

"Deliver this to this address. Give it only to Audrey Herring and wait for a reply," the gentleman said, handing the boy the note along with a coin. There will be another one if you hurry."

"Yes, my lord," the boy said as he took off running.

The man walked into an adjacent room where he grabbed a book and sat down, waiting for the boy to return.

Audrey and Angelique were sitting in the dayroom when the butler entered. "There is a boy at the door wanting to see Lady Audrey."

Audrey gets up and walks to the door to see the boy. "How can I help you?"

"Are you Audrey Herring?" he asked.

"Yes, I am."

The boy handed her the note and stood there. "I have to wait for a reply," he said.

"Come in," she said as she stepped back so he could enter.

She stood there, reading the note, her face growing pale. Then, she walked over to a small table where she took a piece of paper, wrote a short letter, and gave it to the boy.

"Take this back."

"Yes, my lady."

"Thank you," she says as she watches him run out the door.

Audrey walked back into the dayroom and over to Angelique. She looked up as Audrey handed her the note. Angelique read the letter and looked back at Audrey.

"It is time," said Audrey

Angelique nodded.

Two hours later, Audrey left the tea house angry and disgusted after finding out what Ada was planning. Walking up to the carriage, she whispered to her driver about where to take her next. A little later, Jeremy was walking out of the gentlemen's club when a man approached him.

"Sir, my mistress wishes to speak to you." The driver motioned towards the carriage. As he opened the door, Jeremy sees a beautiful blonde woman sitting inside. He looked warily inside the carriage before entering. The carriage started moving, making Jeremy nervous.

"Where are you taking me?"

"Just riding around while we talk. I am Audrey Herring."

"What do you want?"

"I need your help, and you need mine."

"Why do I need your help?"

"Because you got into bed with the wrong woman." Jeremy looked confused. "Ada," she said, tilting her head sideways.

"Do not know what you are talking about," he said, trying to sound firm.

"I know you have been having sex with her for almost a year. It was mainly because you hated Owen, and sleeping with his woman was quite satisfying. I also know what she asked you to do to Veronica Aldridge."

Jeremy tensed, not knowing what to say.

"Do not worry. I do not want to see you hurt. But you are definitely in trouble."

"If you know what she has asked, then you know I said no."

"Yes, but the problem is she will find someone else to do it and could set you up to be blamed."

Jeremy looked away, wondering if Ada would do that to him.

"Yes, she will. You told her no. I have enough spies around to know exactly what she is capable of, and you, dear Jeremy, will now be on her mother's bad side."

"What do I do?" he asked, not sure if he should trust her.

"You help me and do as I say, and you will get out of this unscathed."

"What do you have in mind?"

For the next half hour, they rode around town, talking. Once back at the club, Jeremy opened the door and stepped out, walking toward his home, where he intended to stay until he was needed, wishing he had never met Ada Claridge.

"Things went well?" asked the driver as he checked in on her.

"Yes, perfectly," said Audrey, smiling.

"Where to now?"

"Home. The time has come."

He closed the door and climbed back up, slapping the reins and getting the horses to move. Audrey couldn't help but be excited. It wasn't only about getting her revenge; she also went to see her friends after so many years.

"I am coming for you, Agnes," she said, smiling.

# CHAPTER SEVENTEEN

All facades fall sometimes,
then the mask comes off
and the real heart is seen.

Jessique Whittman

The following day at the Aldridge home, everyone was sitting and eating breakfast when James walked in holding a silver tray.

"A letter for Lady Ellen," he said as he bowed, holding out the tray for Ellen.

She took the letter and read it. Henry noticed her not saying anything as she stared at the paper.

"What does it say?" asked Henry.

"It is from Audrey Herring. She wants to meet at Gordon's Tea Shop today at eleven," she said, still staring at the paper.

"Is that not the woman Veronica mentioned?"

"Yes," she said absent-mindedly.

"What is wrong?"

Ellen handed the letter to Henry.

*Lady Ellen,*

*Please, meet me at Gordon's Tea Shop today at eleven. It is important.*

*Especially yours, Audrey Herring*

"That is Meredith's handwriting, and she always ended her letters with especially yours."

"You sure?" asked Henry.

"Yes, I am."

"If it is her, why use a different name? Maybe, I should go with you."

"No, I will take Michael with me. If she does not want anyone to know, then we do not need to draw attention. You in a tea shop will draw attention," said Ellen, smiling.

"You have a point there. I want William to go as well."

"Okay," she said as she rose from the table and kissed him on the cheek.

Ellen walked into Gordon's a little before eleven. An employee walked up to her.

"Good day, my lady, this way. Lady Herring has already acquired a private room."

Ellen looked around and saw Michael and William at a table in the corner. They nodded their heads at her, signaling that everything was fine. They had arrived early to see who had entered the room.

*They are clever,* she thought, as she followed the employee to a door.

He knocked lightly, then opened it and stepped aside. Ellen walked in and saw a woman sitting at the table. When the woman looked up, she smiled. Ellen's eyes tear up as she looked at the friend she has not seen in years.

"Are you just going to stand there?" asked Audrey as she stood. Ellen hurriedly walked toward her and wrapped her arms around her.

"I have missed you so much," said Ellen

"I have missed you too."

Ellen pulled back and looked at Audrey through tears. "You look beautiful, as always," she said as she wiped her tears.

Before either could say another word, they heard a knock at the door. They both turned to see Eleanor walk in and stop in shock as she saw Audrey.

"Meredith?" she said in a whisper.

"I haven't heard that name in years. Hello Eleanor," she said, smiling.

Eleanor walked up, and they hugged. Ellen walked over and sat at the table, giving them time.

"Let us sit down," said Meredith.

As they sat, Meredith noticed how the two women do not speak to each other.

"Someone want to tell me what happened between you two?"

"You will have to ask Ellen," said Eleanor, not looking up from her teacup.

Audrey looked at Ellen, waiting for an explanation.

"After you left, I went after Agnes. I tried to find evidence that she was the one who hurt you." Eleanor's head popped up hearing Ellen. "I knew she would get back at me by hurting anyone close to me," said Ellen, looking at Eleanor.

"Why did you not tell me?" asked Eleanor, shocked.

"Because you would have wanted to help, and at that time, you had no protection. I was married to Conner, and him being a general, Agnes did not dare come after me. But you had just started with Archie, and I could not risk it."

"But after I was married, you still said nothing."

"You do not know that Archie and Thomas are business partners?" asked Ellen.

Eleanor looked stunned. "No, I do not know about Archie's business affairs. I just thought they were friends."

"Then Conner died, and I had to stay out of Agnes's way. I had, by then, made her an enemy. I am so sorry I hurt you, Eleanor. You have always been dear to me." Eleanor smiled and reached over the table, grabbing Ellen's hand. "After I married Henry, I had Ellis and little Veronica to worry about. So, I had to be very careful."

"Well, that is why we are here. I need to tell you something, Ellen. It will upset you, but you need to stay calm and let me tell you everything, and you cannot let anyone know, especially Henry."

Both women stared at Meredith.

"What is it?" asked Ellen.

Meredith told them about Agnes's plan to take Veronica's money.

"That bitch," said Eleanor.

"This is my fault. If I had not gone after Agnes…"

"No, it is not. Agnes would have gone after Veronica even if Leah were still alive. It is the money she wants. Once Ada is married to Owen, Agnes will have access to it," said Meredith.

"We should have listened to Leah. She warned us to stay away from Agnes," said Eleanor.

Everyone got quiet as they thought of their friend that was no longer with them.

"How do I not tell Henry his daughter is in danger?"

"If you do, you will ruin her plan."

"What plan?"

"Veronica knows. She found out the day she was married."

"That is why Hannah left with Veronica the next morning," said Eleanor.

"She left with Veronica. Are you sure? We thought Owen went with her," said Ellen.

"Yes, Hannah left a note saying something had happened, and she was returning to London with Veronica."

"What happened? How did she find out?" asked Ellen.

Audrey took a deep breath before she continued, knowing it was going to upset them. "Owen spent the night with Ada."

Both women gasped.

"What?!" said Ellen.

"How do you know this? How do you know all of this?" asked Eleanor.

"I have been visiting London for a few years to establish contacts. At first, I was trying to find out who ruined me." She stopped talking, thinking about the past. "And I did."

"Who was it? I tried going through everyone in society for so long and found nothing," said Ellen.

"That is because he was not in society yet. It was a fourteen-year-old boy whose family was on the verge of being thrown out into the street. His father had gambled their family fortune away and left them ruined. He was desperate, and Agnes offered him enough to set his family up for years. But that is a story for another time. I have people everywhere giving me information, and it has served me well as Ada's maid went into her chamber early and saw Owen in her bed."

Tears fell from Ellen's eyes. "My poor baby girl must be heartbroken."

"Veronica is quite surprised. She made a bargain with Owen."

"What kind of bargain?" asked Ellen.

"She would give him her dowry and divorce in exchange for a child."

"Child?" both women said in unison.

"Yes, if Owen gives her a child, then she will agree to the divorce and take all the blame."

"She wants someone to love and who will love her," said Ellen as her heart broke for her daughter.

"I have a plan, but you cannot tell anyone I am here. I need to be able to work unseen," said Meredith.

"Okay," said Eleanor, and Ellen nodded.

"First, we open Owen's eyes to the true Ada. That will definitely be what he deserves," said Audrey as she heard a knock. "And this is the person that will help with that." She got up and opened the door, seeing Jeremy standing behind a man she did not know.

"It is okay, Michael, let him in," said Ellen.

Michael stepped aside and let Jeremy pass. Once the door was closed, Jeremy looked at Meredith. "That guy was scary."

Ellen couldn't help but smile. "Sorry about that. He is my protection."

"That makes sense," he said as he walked to the table.

"Ladies, this is Jeremy. He is going to help us with Owen," said Meredith as they sat down.

For the next hour, Meredith explained her plan, and everyone agreed on their part to play.

Once finished, they left one at a time. First Jeremy, then Meredith.

"Eleanor," said Ellen as she got up from the table.

"Yes?"

"I hope when all this is over, you can forgive me." Ellen stared at Eleanor.

"I already have, but if there is a next time, please do not shut me out. It has been a very lonely sixteen years," said Eleanor with tears in her eyes.

They hugged, and Eleanor left. Ellen sat back down, wondering what she would tell Henry. Finally, she stood, deciding to take one thing at a time. First, she needed to inform Aaron and Ian of the threat to Veronica.

As Owen left the following day to see his solicitor, he was unaware of being followed. Audrey didn't only have spies in people's homes. She had also hired several young boys from the orphanage. They worked in teams and stayed around certain areas. When information needed to be sent, one group would run and hand it to the next group. Meredith knew Veronica had guards who would notice men watching but wouldn't think twice if children were playing in the streets. Today, Meredith needed Owen at the gentlemen's club. So, she sent her runners a message for Owen.

As he was leaving his solicitors, a young boy walked up. "Are you Lord Pierce?"

"Yes."

The boy handed him a letter and took off running. Owen watched the boy as he left. Then he opened the letter and seemed confused as he looked at it. He then flagged down a carriage and told him the destination.

The letter contained one name and a room number, so he went straight there, opening it without knocking.

Owen stopped when he saw a woman and a man sitting at a table. He recognized the man but not the woman.

"What is the meaning of this, Jeremy?" he said as he looked around the room.

"She is not in this room," said the woman, not looking at him.

"Who are you, and where is Ada?"

"My name is Audrey Herring, and we need to speak to you. Please sit down," she said as she turned around.

"I do not know you and do not wish to speak to either of you," said Owen as he turned to leave.

"You do not wish to know the truth about Ada?" asked Jeremy.

"I would not believe anything you have to say."

"Then look for yourself," said Audrey as she walked over and slid back a panel in the wall.

Owen slowly walked over and looked through it—and froze. He couldn't believe what he was seeing. Ada was in bed with another man.

"It cannot be. She would not do this," Owen said as he turned around to face Audrey.

"She is not the sweet girl she led you to believe," said Jeremy.

"How would you know?" Owen growled.

"Because I have been sleeping with her for the last year." Jeremy looked down, feeling guilty. He thought it would feel good to hurt Owen, but surprisingly, it didn't.

Owen stood, not saying a word.

"I know you do not want to believe this, but Ada is looking for someone to hurt Veronica. Two days ago, I was in that room with her, and she asked me to compromise Veronica so you would question who the baby's father is."

Owen grew pale and seemed to lose his balance. Jeremy and Audrey both grabbed him and sat him down.

"Just breath," said Audrey as she knelt beside him.

"I know this is a lot to take in, but you have to understand Ada is not a good person. She has been making you out to be a fool. I am sorry to be so blunt with this," Audrey said.

"I do not understand," Owen said as all of what he had seen and heard was too much for him to grasp.

"Okay, let us start from the beginning. Jeremy, tell him the entire story about you and Ada," said Audrey as she sat back down.

"Ada and I started talking over a year ago. I wanted to court her, but her mother would not allow it. I am only inheriting the title of a baron, and Agnes demanded more than that."

"And I am going to be an earl," said Owen as he sat up straight.

"Yes. We continued our affair in secret until the other day when she asked me to hurt Veronica. After that, I ended it because I wanted to live. Aldridge's daughter would be a sure way to die."

"Why does she want to hurt Veronica and my baby?'

"If the child's paternity were in question, he would inherit nothing," said Audrey.

Owen took a deep breath, trying to control the contents of his stomach to stay down. "Is all of this true? Please, if it is not, say so. I do not know how to deal with this," said Owen as he looked at both of them.

"I wish it was not. It makes me sick to think about what they want to do to such a sweet person," said Audrey.

Owen thought of Veronica and how he had hurt her. For what? He finally realized what a fool he had been. "Who is that in there with her?"

"That is a footman from one of the lords that frequent this establishment. She is getting him to do what I refused," said Jeremy.

"She is a whore," whispered Owen.

Everyone stayed quiet, giving Owen time to accept everything.

"I have to protect Veronica. She has been hurt enough by this, by me," Owen said.

"We have a plan, but the only thing we will do right now is protect Veronica. You need to go home and act like everything is okay," Audrey said.

"Why? Should I not be taking Veronica away from here?"

"Because we will wait until Veronica is a few months pregnant. That way, when we expose Agnes and Ada for who they are, there will be no threat to the child. So, you need to go home and act normal," Audrey said.

"I cannot even warn Veronica?'

"No, we have already informed her guards, and Ellen has sent hers also."

"Lady Ellen knows?"

"Yes, but Henry does not, and we want to keep it that way for now."

"Okay," said Owen as he thought about protecting Veronica and the child they might have.

"That also means you have to act normal around Ada. You cannot let her know you are on to her plan. Can you do that?" asked Audrey.

"I don't know. I want to remove her head."

"You have to remain calm. Then you will get your chance to confront her."

"What is in this for you? Why are you doing this?" asked Owen.

Audrey took a deep breath. "I was the daughter of a viscount. Agnes set me up because she wanted the man I was going to marry," she said as she looked down. It still hurt her to think of Thomas.

Jeremy and Owen both looked at her, surprised.

"Thomas Claridge?" asked Owen.

"Yes. After I was compromised, my father threw me out. If it were not for my friend, I would have been living on the street."

"Wow," said Jeremy.

"All right, I will do as you say. It will not make Ada suspicious if I stay away from her. We had already agreed to keep our distance until the divorce."

"Good," said Audrey as she stood.

Both men stood and walked towards the door to leave.

"I will keep Veronica at home," said Owen.

"No, you have to act like everything is normal. That means being in society. Ada wants her plan to happen in front of as many people as possible. Do not worry, no harm will come to her," said Audrey as she put her hand on his shoulder. She then turned and left.

"Owen, I know we have never liked each other, but I am sorry for my part in all of this. I wish I had never laid eyes on Ada," said Jeremy.

"Me too," said Owen as they left the room.

That night Owen was sitting by the fireplace watching the fire, thinking about everything he had learned. He couldn't believe he had been such a fool. Once it was over, he would have to apologize to Ellis. So many times, Ellis tried to warn him about Ada, but he wouldn't listen.

Veronica walked in and saw Owen in deep thought. She went over and touched his shoulder, causing him to jump.

"I did not hear you come in."

"Are you all right?"

"Yes, I have a few things on my mind," Owen said as he stood.

"Anything you want to talk about?"

"No. You ready for bed?"

"Yes. I came in to tell you I was going to my room."

"Will I see you tonight?"

"Yes," she said, blushing.

He walked over and kissed her forehead. Veronica watched him leave, knowing he was hiding something, but she wouldn't dwell on it. After she has her baby, his problems would be his problems.

She then left to get ready.

# CHAPTER NINETEEN

Deceiving others. That's what
the world calls romance.

Oscar Wilde

A week later, a ball was being held at The Carlisle home. That was the first time Owen and Veronica would go as husband and wife. Knowing they would be the center of attention worried Veronica. Would they be able to act like a loving couple?

"You seem nervous," said Owen as they sat in the carriage on the way to the ball.

"Can you act as if you care about me?" asked Veronica, not looking at him.

He reaches over and takes her hand. "I do care about you."

"Okay," said Veronica, smiling at him.

The ball was in full swing when Veronica and Owen walked in. Everyone stopped, including the dancers, causing the music to stop as well. Owen put his arm around her waist, pulling her closer.

Lord Carlisle walked up and bowed. "Welcome, Lord and Lady Pierce. Thank you so much for gracing us with your appearance," he said excitedly.

"Thank you for the invitation," said Owen.

"Please, enjoy yourself. If there is anything you need, ask." Lord Carlisle stepped aside.

"Thank you," said Veronica as Owen led her further inside, not letting go of her hand. Veronica concentrated on her breathing to seem calm. Then she saw Hannah and Dinah walking towards her, and she smiled.

"So glad you made it," said Hannah as they hugged her.

The music started back up, and everyone returned to doing what they were doing, as if nothing had interrupted them.

"I am going to let you ladies talk while I go say hello to Ellis," said Owen as he bowed, then walked off.

"How are you?" asked Dinah.

Veronica looked at her for a second. "I am good, and you?"

"I am okay." Dinah was worried that Veronica hated her. They had not spoken since the wedding.

"We will talk about things later, but tonight, we will enjoy the ball," said Veronica. Dinah nodded her head and looked up as Johnathan Tisdale walked up and asked her to dance.

"You are going to forgive her?" asked Hannah.

"Yes, I will. But, of course, I cannot say things will be as they were, but she will be my child's aunt, so we need to be friendly."

Hannah looked down, wishing things could return to how they were.

"Would you care to dance?" Hannah looked and saw Ellis standing there with his hand out. She put her hand in his, and he led her toward the dance floor.

"Well, wife, would you do me the honor?" said Owen, smiling. She smiled back and took his hand.

As everyone watched, they seemed to have affection for each other, pleasing most of the crowd. Only two were not smiling. Agnes and Ada stood to the side, watching Owen and Veronica as they danced.

"Are you sure Owen has not developed a tendre for her?" asked Agnes.

"It does not matter. After tonight, it will be over, and we will have the money," said Ada as she walked towards the hall.

Once the dance had stopped, Veronica wiped her forehead. "I am a little tired. Think I will go rest for a bit."

"Okay, be careful," said Owen as Ellis and Hannah walked up.

Veronica walked toward the hall, wondering where the sitting room was. As she turned the corner, she saw Ada standing there with a smile on her face.

"You have something to say, so go ahead," said Veronica.

"I was wondering how it felt to know the man you married never will care about you," said Ada as she walked closer, so no one would hear her.

"Oh, Ada, you and your games. Do you not realize the precarious situation you have put yourself in?"

"What do you mean?'

"The only reason you will get what you want is that I have allowed it."

"You think so?" said Ada as her eyes narrowed.

"All I have to do is tell everyone about you and your mother's plan, or better yet. I could say you are Owen's mistress. Then, nobody would blame me for getting a divorce. You, of course, will be ruined."

"Nobody would believe you," said Ada with a smug look.

"Why? Because you are such a nice person? Tell me how many have you hurt and are sitting and waiting for an opportunity to see you fall?"

Ada's face grew pale as Veronica smiled and leaned in to whisper in her ear.

"You will stay away from Owen until we are divorced. This will be my only warning. If you disrespect me again in any way, I will teach you a lesson you will never forget." Veronica backed away and smiled. She then turned and walked down the hall.

Ada was stunned, thinking Veronica wasn't that weak little kitten she always pretended to be.

*Keep believing you are winning. Soon, you will be finished,* she thought as she turned and went back to the ball.

Earlier, Ian and Aaron arrived at the stables behind the Carlisle home to meet William and Michael. Knowing a footman would hurt Veronica, Aaron, and Ian would hide in the carriage stable while Michael and William snuck into the house. Sitting in the shadows for hours was something they were trained to do. They had seen and done enough to know the evil in the world and would willingly give their lives for an angel like Veronica.

A couple of hours into the ball, they saw someone sneaking through the shadows, making his way to the back of the house. Ian followed while Aaron stayed back in case it was the wrong person.

As the person entered the window, Ian snuck up and watched until he had left the room before following. Michael and William were hiding in separate rooms, peeking out the door when they saw someone coming out of a room, making his way to the room across from the resting room.

For a while, they watched as women came and left. Finally, they saw Veronica coming down the hall.

As she turned to enter the room, he jumped out and hit her on the back of the head, causing her to collapse into his arms. All three men leaped into action and were in the room before the man could lay Veronica on the floor. Michael and Ian grabbed him as William went straight to Veronica.

In the ballroom, Owen saw Ada standing with her friends, smiling at him. He looked around, noticing Veronica was not back yet. Excusing himself, Owen walked out of the ball, trying not to draw attention. But before he could reach the sitting room, he saw William stick his head out, motioning him to enter. Once inside the room, he saw Ian and Michael standing over a tied-up man and Veronica lying on a couch, not moving.

"Is she all right?" Owen asked as he ran to her and held her hand.

"Yes, just knocked out. She should wake up any time," said William as he walked over to the other two.

Owen watched as they dragged the man to the side window.

"We know what to do with him," said William as he followed out the window.

Veronica started moaning and moving her head as she began to wake. Owen put his hand on her face as her eyes opened. She shot up and looked around, not knowing what was happening.

"Sweetheart, it is okay. You are okay."

"Owen? Someone hit me."

"I know. You are safe now," he said as he wrapped his arms around her. She laid her head on his chest and relaxed. "Can you stand?"

"Yes, I think so."

Owen stood and helped her up.

"My head hurts."

Owen put his hand on her head and felt through her hair. "I feel a small knot, but it is not bleeding. Let us get your hair pinned back up. Some of it is down," Owen said as he walked her to the mirror.

"Who tried to hurt me?" she said as she fixed her hair.

"I will explain everything when we get home."

As they walked toward the door, it swung open, and Ada came in with a few of her friends. She thought she would walk in on something scandalous but was shocked to see Owen and Veronica in the room alone.

"What were you doing in here?" asked Ada, wondering what had gone wrong. Why did Veronica look okay?

"Can a husband and wife not have some time alone?" said Owen trying to control his anger. He knew Ada was trying to catch Veronica in a compromising situation.

Veronica had a bad feeling looking at Ada. That wasn't coincidental. First, someone attacked her, and now Ada walked in with her friends. She looked up and was surprised at Owen, looking furious.

"Sorry to intrude," said Ada as she left with her friends.

"Come on, let us's say our goodbyes and go home," said Owen as he put his arm around her waist.

"All right," she said as they left the room.

The guards dragged the tied-up man into a room at the side of the stable, putting him in the corner. Ian lit a lantern and brought it over. William removed the gag and was shocked when he saw his face.

"Bloody hell, it is a kid," he said as he stepped back.

"How old are you?" asked Ian.

"Sixteen," he said, not looking up.

"You look younger than that," said Michael.

"Why did you want to hurt Veronica Aldridge?" asked Ian.

"My master said he would set me free."

"Who is your master?"

"Malcolm Randolph," he said in a whisper.

They all looked at each other. Malcolm was well known for his cruelty and rumored to take advantage of his servants. Girls and boys.

"What is your name?" asked Michael.

"John Tillman," he says as he looks up at the men surrounding him. "I was not going to hurt her as he told me to. I was just going to make it look bad."

"Why do you want your freedom?" asked William.

John looked back at the ground, not wanting to tell them what had happened to him.

"It is okay. You can tell us," said Ian in a soft voice.

"He hurts me," was all he said in a low voice.

Ian bent down and untied him.

"Are you going to kill me?" he asked but didn't sound scared, more hopeful that his pain would end.

"No, we are taking you to a place where you will be safe," said William.

"Really?"

"Yes, but you must do as we say." William turned to the other men. "We have to get out of here without being seen. Ian, tell Aaron what has happened, and we will meet you back home. Owen has probably already left with Miss Veronica."

"Okay," said Ian as he quickly left the room.

"Now, stay behind us and be as quiet as you can," said William.

"Yes, sir," said John.

They snuck out, and John stayed right behind, being very quiet.

On the way home, Veronica didn't say a word. Owen watched her, not knowing what to say. He knew he would have to tell her everything when they got home, which scared him. But she deserved the truth.

Once home, they went into the sitting room, where Owen poured two glasses of bourbon as Veronica sat in a chair next to the fire. Owen handed her a drink before he sat in a chair on the other side.

"Tell me what is going on."

"Ada tried to have you compromised tonight," said Owen, staring at the fire.

"Why, I thought we had an accord?"

"I had nothing to do with it." He then told her everything he had found out and how.

"They did not want me to know?"

"Not until you were pregnant and far enough along that the scandal could not hurt the baby. I am so sorry. I am such a fool."

Veronica was quiet as she thought about everything he had told her. They heard a knock, then Elliot walked in.

"My lady, the boys are here and need to talk to you."

"Send them in," she said as she stood and moved to the couch.

As they walked in, she saw they had someone unfamiliar following behind.

"Who is this?"

"This is John. He is the one that tried to hurt you tonight," said Aaron.

"What! You brought him here?" yelled Owen as he got up and went for John. All four men stepped in front, protecting him.

Veronica knew there was a reason they had brought him there. She looked closer and realized he was young and scared. "Owen, stop," she said.

"He tried to hurt you."

"Just wait. Come here," she said, waving John over. He slowly walked forward as the guys moved out of the way.

"Sit," she said, pointing to the chair across from the couch. "Your name is John?"

"John Tillman. People call me Johnny," he said, not looking up.

"Miss, may I speak?" asked Ian.

"Yes."

"He was ordered to hurt you by Malcolm Randolph."

Veronica looked at Owen. "That monster!" she said.

Owen walked over but stopped, holding his hands up when the guys moved to stop him. "I'm just going to sit by Veronica."

They stepped back, watching him until he sat down on the couch.

"Randolph was the one who was supposed to hurt Veronica, but he ordered you to do it?" asked Owen.

"Yes, he told me if I did this, he would set me free," said Johnny, still not looking up.

"Look up," said Veronica.

He slowly raised his head. "I am sorry," he said, looking at Veronica.

"We know about Randolph. You want away from him?"

"Yes, ma'am."

"There will be a time in a few months when we will expose the culprits. Will you be willing to tell your story about tonight?" asked Owen.

"He will kill me." Johnny started moving uncomfortably in his seat.

"That will not work. It is his word against Malcolm's," she said, looking at Owen. "Did you ever see or hear Ada talk to Malcolm?" asked Veronica.

He blushed and looked down. "I was in the room when he forced her. He likes people to watch."

"That is why they thought she was in there with a footman," Owen said, looking at Veronica.

"You said forced her? Was she unwilling to be with him?" asked Veronica.

Johnny nodded his head yes.

"He is disgusting," said Veronica.

"We have to find a safe place," said Ian.

"Johnny, I have a home in Scotland. Would you be willing to work for me there?"

"Yes, ma'am," he said, looking up.

"Do you like being a footman?" she asked.

"I like horses."

"Good. I need a groomsman," she said, smiling. "I need one of you to take him tonight." She looked at the guys.

"I will take him," said Ian.

"Take one of the carriages with the Aldridge crest. Nobody will stop you."

Ian and the rest left the room to prepare for the journey.

"Miss?" said Johnny as he stood.

"Yes?"

"Thank you."

"This is a chance for you. Work hard, and you will be treated well. I promise," she said, smiling.

"Yes, ma'am," he said with a big smile, the happiest he had been in years.

It wasn't long before they pulled out on their way out of London.

Back at the ball, Ada was not in a good mood.

"Why the long face?" asked Agnes as she walked up.

"Something went wrong. Veronica is unharmed," she snarled.

"I know. Randolph did not want to get his hands dirty, so he sent his footman to do it. Now he cannot find him. Do not worry. Nobody can trace it back to me. Now they will be on guard."

"Well, we will wait for the divorce. Then Owen and the money will be yours," said Ada.

"Do not fret. Even if she has a boy, things happen to children all the time," Agnes said as she walked away.

Ada stared at her mother. Hurt a child? Surely, she didn't mean that. Ada felt sick and went to get something to drink, trying to forget what her mother had just said.

# CHAPTER TWENTY

She wasn't looking for a knight,
She was looking for a sword.

Atticus

Late one night, Feagin and Murray walked into a tavern on White Chapel. Murray had to breathe through his mouth to keep from smelling the foul stench of the place. They walked over to a table where several men sat.

"Parnell," said a man, who—even though he wore expensive clothes—one could tell he hadn't bathed in weeks. His hair was greasy and stuck to his head, teeth yellow and probably breath to match.

"Blakely," said Feagin as he sat down.

"Why did you want to meet?" asked Blakely as he waved the other men to leave.

Murray stood behind Feagin, watching in case there was trouble. As he looked around, he saw a couple in the far corner. A girl was straddling a man, and it was apparent what they were doing. Once the man finished, the girl stood and straightened her gown. Then, after being paid, she turned and walked away toward Murray. He realizes she couldn't be older than twelve.

When she got close, he looked away, feeling guilty because he knew she probably wouldn't live to see eighteen, and there was nothing he could do about it. Unfortunately, there were so many like her.

"I am here to talk about a problem we have."

"What is that?"

"A certain person who keeps taking our employees."

Blakely laughs.

"What do you think we can do about it?"

"I have been looking for two years and found nothing. Then I heard you had a problem a few months back."

"Yeah, I had lost some small people I found."

Murray knew found meant stolen. Blakely was known for dealing in children. He would slit his throat and lose no sleep over it if he could.

"There has to be someone giving him information, and there has to be a connection. So, we need to find it."

"He is not that easy to capture. The last time two of my men were put down for a week. The people around here call them ghosts."

"Them?"

"Yes. My men came upon two people taking my property, then, out of the shadows, were more. They swore they never saw them."

"Where did you find your small people?"

Blakely leaned forward and kept his voice low. "The orphanage on King's Road."

"King's Road," said Feagin as he looked off, thinking. Then his head popped back to Blakely. "I think we just found out where it is coming from," he said, smiling.

Murray stopped breathing. He's figured it out. Amy lived by that orphanage before Feagin set his sights on her.

"Sit down, Murray. I need you on this," said Feagin, motioning to the seat next to him.

Murray sat down and listened as they came up with a plan. He was glad Feagin wanted him to be a part of it. It might cost him his life, but he had to interfere with their trap. He couldn't let Feagin find Amy and his son.

A couple of weeks later, everything was going smoothly. Veronica and Owen did not attend any more social functions, and they heard nothing from Malcolm Randolph. A man watched the house for several days, but that stopped. Malcolm must have thought Johnny was dead.

"You know, eventually, you are going to run into Owen," said Veronica as Lydia helped her undress.

"I have not' thought about it lately," said Lydia with a sad look on her face.

"What is wrong? Is everything all right with you and Adrian?"

"I love him," said Lydia as tears started running down her face.

Veronica reached over and hugged her. Then, she pulled back and wiped Lydia's face. "Now, tell me what is wrong."

"I am scared. What if Adrian decides to take back what is his?"

"Oh, Lydia, Adrian adores you. Are you afraid he will leave you behind?"

"Yes. Veronica, I am just a maid now."

"Lydia, Adrian would never do that to you. Have you talked to him about this? Has he said anything about wanting to go back?"

"No," she said, looking down.

"That is something you have to do. It is going to eat you up if you do not'," said Veronica as she held Lydia's face.

"All right."

Then they heard a light tap on the door. Lydia walked over and saw Amy with a letter. Veronica walked up and took it from her.

"We go tonight," she said after reading it.

"Really? It has been a while since we got one of those," said Lydia as she opened the trunk.

"Amy, wait," said Veronica as she went to her vanity, pulled out some paper, and started writing. "Take this to Owen's valet."

"Yes, ma'am," said Amy as she curtsied and walked off.

"What did you say?"

"Just not feeling like coming tonight. So put some pillows on my bed as we did at Father's. But first, go tell the men."

Ian and Michael left before the others to check out the address Veronica had received. Once there, they realized it was down an alley. However, it wasn't a dead end, so they decided to come up to the other side to see the situation.

They found a couple of hiding places and crouched across from each other. Ian heard something coming from behind them and slowly pulled out his pistol. Something seemed wrong as he watched the shadows. As soon as Ian saw the pistol, he fired. A man slumped out from the dark, and his pistol fired before he hit the ground.

"Ian," Michael whispered. Ian looked over and saw Michael holding his shoulder. The bullet from the man's gun had hit Michael. Ian ran to him and helped him up.

"It is a trap. Can you run?"

"Yes."

Michael stayed right with Ian even though his shoulder was hurting something awful. When they reached their horses, Ian helped Michael mount and then went to his. "We have to get back and warn Veronica before they leave."

After getting back, Ian helped Michael off his horse as Clare came out the kitchen door.

"What happened?" she asked.

"It was a trap. Where is Miss Veronica?" asked Ian.

"She already left."

"Take Michael inside. I have to stop them," said Ian as he mounted his horse and took off.

Veronica stood outside the carriage and looked down the alley.

"Aaron, stay here."

"Why?"

"I need you ready in case we need to make a quick getaway."

"Are you sure?"

"Yes. Pull the carriage up so as not to draw attention here," said Veronica as she started walking into the alley. She walked slowly, staying to the side, crouching down behind anything she could find. She froze when she reached the door as three men stepped out of the shadows.

Veronica turned immediately and started running back, but before she got very far, something hit her back, throwing her to the ground and hitting her head hard.

*Was I shot?* she thought before darkness took her.

"What did you do?" Murray yelled at the man who held the pistol.

"He was getting away."

"Feagin wanted him alive. Now you can tell him what you did," said Murray as he walked to the unmoving Veronica.

Bending down, he noticed his hat had come off and saw braided hair wrapped around his head. He thought it couldn't be as he raised Veronica's shirt and saw the binding bounding her breasts.

"Oh god," he whispered as he picked her up bridal style.

"What are you doing?" asked one of the men.

"He is alive. I am taking him to the doctor. Go tell Feagin what has happened," he said as he turned to leave, hoping they believed him.

As soon as he reached the end of the alley, he saw a carriage waiting down the street, hoping it was hers. When he grew close, a man exited, and his eyes widened.

"What happened?" asked Aaron.

"She has been shot. Get in, and I will hand her to you."

Once they got her in, Aaron laid her face down, seeing her bleeding back. Murray entered behind him.

"Lift the lid in that seat and look for something to apply pressure to her wound." Once Murray was applying pressure, Aaron jumped out and climbed up to the seat, taking the reins and hitting the horses hard to get the carriage moving as fast as it would go.


Owen's valet entered his bedroom and walked over to a sleeping Owen.

"My lord, wake up," said Edgar as he lightly shook him.

Owen groggily opened his eyes. "What is wrong?" he said, sitting up.

"You need to come with me. Miss Veronica is hurt."

Hearing that, Owen jumped up and grabbed his robe. "Where is she?"

"This way," said Edgar as he ran down the stairs towards the servants' quarters.

Owen entered the room and saw all the servants standing around the bed. When they saw him, they moved to let him see Veronica. She was face down, shirtless, and a man removed a bullet from her back.

"What the hell is going on?" Owen said as he walked up to the side of the bed. "What happened to her?"

"She was shot," Adrian said as he dropped the bullet in a pan.

"Who are you, and how did this happen?" Owen said, getting angry.

"Both those questions are a long story. But know, I am a doctor," said Adrian as he prepared to sew the wound up.

"Let us start from the beginning," said Clare.

"Who are you?"

"I am Clare, the cook. Three years ago, my husband and I were fired from our former jobs," said Clare as Elliot stepped up beside her.

"The truth is, our former boss tried to take liberties with her, and he threw us out with nothing. I finally got to work, but it was not' the legal kind. So, one day, my boss wanted Clare to work for him, and I refused. Two men held me while the boss dragged Clare down an alley. Then, out of nowhere, this girl came up and started fighting the boss. She knocked him out cold, removed a knife from his belt, and threatened the men holding me. They ran like scared girls, and we followed her to a coach, and she brought us here. That is when it all started."

"When what started? Somebody, explain to me what is going on," said Owen as he ran his hands through his hair.

"Maybe my story will make sense," said a girl sitting on the bed beside Veronica as she turned her head so Owen could see her face.

"Lydia!" What are you doing here, and why are you dressed as a maid?"

"I am a maid. I am Veronica's lady's maid."

"I do not' understand. You are the daughter of an Earl. Please explain."

"After my father died, my cousin paid the solicitor to change his will. My mother and I were left with nothing. My cousin said I could stay as long as I married whomever he chose. My mother refused, and he threw us out. I at least hid enough jewels in my clothes to pay for a few months' rent."

"Why did' you not come to me?" asked Owen.

"I went to your house and met your mother. Ann had already been told not to help me. She would ensure the wrath of the ton if she did."

"My mother turned you away?"

"I then went to Ada. I thought she was my best friend, but she stood there and laughed. It saved her from having to get rid of me herself," said Lydia, looking down.

"What do you mean?"

"I was in her way. She wanted you."

Owen's hatred for Ada grew the more he found out about her.

"Owen, I could not' even find work. Nobody would help us, and our money was running out. Mother grew sick, and I did not' know what to do. Then, one day, she told me she had sent a message to someone that would save me. I had no idea who that could be until I opened our door, and there stood Veronica. She brought us here and took care of my mother until she died. I did not' want to return to society, so Veronica offered me this position.

"ut is what she does. She saves people," said Lydia as she stroked Veronica's hair. "After everything Aa and I did to her. We were horrible to her, and she still came to help me."

Owen looked around the room at all the servants.

"All of you?" he asked.

Amy stepped forward. "We all have different stories, but the ending is the same. Veronica saved us all."

The door opened, and Ian, Aaron, and Murry walked in.

"Murray?" said Amy as she ran into his arms.

Everyone stood watching, wondering who that was. Finally, Adrian finished, pulled the sheet over her back, and stood.

"What happened out there?" asked Adrian.

"It was a trap," said Ian.

"Feagin figured out someone at the orphanage was sending information. I did not' count on one of Blakely's men to shoot," said Murray, not taking his eyes off Amy.

"I have missed you," she said, buried in his chest.

"Do 'you not work for Parnell? I believe I kicked you in the chest when we rescued Amy," said Adrian.

"Yes, I did work for him, but not anymore. When you came for Amy that day, I had to make it look convincing. I had to get her and my son to safety. I never thought I would see you again," he said as he hugged her tighter.

"Mama," said Little John as he walked into the room, rubbing his sleepy eyes.

"John, why are you up," said Amy as she picked him up.

"I not find you," he said as he laid his head on her shoulder and went back to sleep.

Murray looked at John with so much love in his eyes as he touched his head.

"Let us go to my room and get out of their way," said Amy as she took his hand and led them out of the room.

Owen walked over and sat down beside Veronica.

"Why did' she not tell me? I would have protected her," Owen said as he held her hand.

"You would have stopped her. She does not' think she needs protection. She is so brave. Does not' ever think about herself," said Lydia as she stood beside Adrian.

Adrian put his arm around her and pulled her up next to him. Everyone started leaving the room after hearing Veronica was going to make it. Only Lydia and Adrian were left in the room with Owen.

"Who are you? Have we met before?" asked Owen, looking at Adrian.

"Adrian Cartwright."

Owen's eyes grew big. "Earl of Essex? You are supposed to be dead."

"Yes. That is what my brother was hoping to accomplish."

"Your brother?"

"Yes, I had just left my business manager one night when two men attacked me. They thought I was dying and happily told me my brother wanted me dead. The funny thing is, I never wanted the title. I would have given it to him if he asked," said Adrian, looking down, sadness evident on his face.

Lydia wrapped her arms around his waist and laid her head on his chest.

"I am sorry that happened to you," said Owen, looking back toward Veronica. "How did you and Veronica meet?"

"An old woman found me in an alley. She thought I was dead at first. I do not' know how she got me to her home, but when I woke, I saw Veronica. Once I was able to move, she brought me here. All I ever wanted to be was a doctor, and Veronica has ensured I stay busy," he said as he looked at the sleeping Veronica.

"She will be out for a while. So, you should also get some rest," said Adrian.

"Yes, Owen. I will stay with her tonight." Lydia walked over to stand by Owen.

"Okay, but come get me as soon as she wakes," said Owen as he stood.

"I will," she said as she sat down beside Veronica.

"Thank you, Lord Cartwright." Owen as he held out his hand.

"'ut Adrian," he replied, shaking his hand.

After Owen left, Adrian walked up beside Lydia and stared at Veronica.

"She has to stop," said Lydia.

"Yes, she does. Especially now that I believe she is pregnant."

"What?! Pregnant?"

"Yes, her heartbeat is higher than normal. I did not' want to say anything to Owen just yet. It is still early, and with everything that happened tonight, she could have a miscarriage."

"Oh, I hope not. She deserves a little happiness."

"Stay with her. I need to check on Michael," said Adrian as he left the room.

Veronica slept through the night without waking. When her eyes opened, she tried to move but stopped when pain shot through her back. She lay there trying to remember what had happened. The only thing that came to mind was her running down an alley.

Slowly she moved to turn over. Finally, she lay on her back, looked around, and realized she was in a servants' room. After a few minutes, she tried to sit up but laid back when her head started pounding.

Lydia walked in carrying clothes when she noticed Veronica was awake. "Good, you are awake. I brought you some clothes. How are you feeling?"

"What happened? Why am I here?"

"You walked into a trap where you were shot. Once they returned with you, this was the closest room so Adrian could get the bullet out."

"Oh," Veronica said as she tried to sit up.

"NO, do not' try to move. You could open your stitches." Lydia pushed your back down.

"Can you at least help me get dressed? I feel very uncomfortable without a shirt on in the servants' quarters."

"Okay, we can do that. Are you hungry?" Lydia asked after Veronica finished dressing.

"A little, I think."

"Okay, I will go get you some soup, and Owen wanted me to inform him when you are awake."

"Is he angry?" asked Veronica, trying to find a comfortable way to lie.

"No, I think he is in shock. He now knows how you have helped everyone here. I finally talked to him and told him what had happened to me."

"How did he take it?"

"He seemed to be angry at Ada. I am so glad he finally knows the truth about her. I am going to go. Do you need anything else?"

"No, just some soup."

A few minutes later, there was a knock at the door.

"Come in."

The door opened, and Owen walked in, looking like he 'hadn't slept.

"How are you feeling?' Owen asked as he walked over and sat in a chair beside the bed.

"I am okay. My back hurts, but other than that, I am good."

"Why would you do something so dangerous?"

"People need help."

"And you have to be the one to help them?"

"Yes, when I can."

"Not anymore," he said, getting up, obviously angry.

"I will do as I deem fit. You cannot stop me," she retorted.

"Veronica, you were shot and could have died. Then what? To think you want to have a baby. Are you still going to do this when you are pregnant, risking your own child's life?"

"No, of course not," she whispered, looking down.

He took a deep breath to calm down, walked back, and sat down. "I do not' want to argue. But, when I saw Adrian pulling a bullet out of your back, it scared me," he said, looking her in the eyes.

Before he could say anymore, someone knocked. Owen went and opened the door.

"Can we come in?" asked Adrian.

It was apparent they had heard them arguing.

"Yes," said Veronica, welcoming the interruption.

Adrian and Ian, along with Lydia carrying a bowl, walked in.

"How are you feeling?" asked Adrian as he walked towards the bed.

"I feel fine except for the pain in my back and a slight headache," she said, looking at Owen.

Lydia wanted to laugh but held it in.

"What about your lower stomach? Any discomfort?"

"No." She looked at him, confused.

"Good. I did not' say anything last night because I wanted to be sure there were not' any complications."

"Complications?" asked Owen.

"I am pretty sure you are pregnant," said Adrian, smiling at Veronica.

Everyone was quiet.

"How do you know? We have not' been married but for a little over two months," said Veronica.

"You were out, and still, your heartbeat was fast. When was your last cycle?"

Veronica thought, and then her eyes grew wide. "It was two weeks before I got married."

"You must have conceived your first time then," said Adrian.

"Congratulations," said Ian.

"Okay, to be safe, Veronica, I need you to stay in bed for a few days. Your body has been through a lot, and we do not' want you to miscarry. Okay?"

Veronica looked up at Adrian, her smile falling. "Could I lose it?"

"We are going to make sure you do not'," Adrian said as he held her wrist, feeling her pulse.

Her smile came back, and she looked at everyone in the room. "Ian, what happened?"

"It was a trap. Feagin Parnell figured out about the orphanage."

"Oh no, the orphanage."

"It is okay. We have moved everyone to a safe place for now. But we need to find another permanent place."

"There is a house I had recently purchased outside of London near Cornwall. Owen can give you the location. I think it is best to sell the house on King's Road. I 'will not be using it anymore," she said, rubbing her stomach.

"You are going to be a father," said Lydia as she nudged Owen.

"I am going to be a father," he said more to himself than anybody else.

Ian padded him on the back. "Yes, you are."

"Okay, I need to check her wound," said Adrian letting everyone know they needed to leave.

"Lydia, will you help her to turn over?" he asked as Owen and Ian left the room, laughing and talking about being a father.

After checking her back, Lydia helped her lie back down.

"It looks good. I need you to rest, understand?"

"Yes, I will."

"Okay, I need to check on Michael."

"What happened to Michael?"

"I will tell her," said Lydia.

Adrian bent down, kissed Lydia on the forehead, and left the room.

"Okay, what happened to Michael?"

"First, he is going to be okay. He was shot last night. That is why they were not' there. Ian tried to get back and stop you from going, but it was too late. You had already left." She sat in the chair beside the bed. "Veronica, I was scared to death when I saw Aaron walk in, and behind him was a big guy carrying you. Blood dripping on the floor."

"What big guy?"

"Oh, you do not' know about Murray? I am not sure about the details, but he was one of Parnell's men. He saved you from what I heard, and he is Amy's husband."

"Amy's husband? Little John's father?"

"Yes."

"I would like to talk to him."

"Now?"

"Yes, I do not' have anything else to do."

"Okay, I will go and get him. Here is your soup. You need to eat it all. We need a strong baby," Lydia said as she handed Veronica the bowl.

"What is with this 'we'?"

"It is my godchild. I have a say in the little fellow," said Lydia as she left the room.

Veronica couldn't help but smile. She was so thankful to have Lydia in her life.

A few minutes later, Lydia knocked and opened the door.

"They are here, if you still want to talk."

"Yes, let them in," she said as she set the bowl on the table beside the bed.

Ian, Amy, and Murray walked in and stood at the foot of the bed. Lydia 'hadn't been exaggerating; Murray was tall and very muscular.

"Grab those chairs over there," she said as she pointed to the corner. "I am uncomfortable with everyone standing."

After everyone sat, Veronica noticed Murray was looking down and holding Ann's hand tightly.

"Sir, what is your name?"

"Murray Cochran," he replied, not looking up.

"You are Amy's husband. She told me about you. You can look at me. I am not mean." As he looked up, she gave him a big smile. He seemed to relax. "Why did you save me? You could have let me die. It would have protected Amy's whereabouts for good."

Murray looked back down. He seemed to be thinking about what to say.

"My dad was a brutal man. He would get mad and hurt my mother. She made me promise never to hurt a girl. I thought you were a boy until your hat fell off, and I saw your braid. If you had lived the things Feagin would have done to you...I could not' let that happen."

"Parnell will be looking for you," she said more as a statement, not a question.

"Yes, ma'am."

Everyone got quiet as Veronica seemed to be in deep thought.

"London is no longer safe for you. We need to get you and your family out. I have a home in Scotland. Would you be willing to work for me there?"

"Oh, John loved it there. He had so much fun exploring the castle," said Amy, smiling.

"Castle?" asked Murray.

"Yes, it is a castle. Unfortunately, it is not fully staffed since I have not' been going there much in the last few years. ut after my baby is born, I intend to move there to live, and I need people I can trust."

"Are you pregnant?" asked Amy.

"Yes, we just found out today," said Veronica, smiling.

"Congratulations."

"Thank you. Well, Murray, what do you say?"

"I would like that a lot," said Murray smiling for the first time since entering the room.

"I will take them. I need to check on Johnny also," said Ian.

"Good. I am so glad to have both of you there with me. I can never repay you for saving my life, but I promise you, work hard for me and be loyal, and I will take care of you and your family."

"No, ma'am. You owe me nothing. You saved my family. It is I that owes you, and I promise with my life, you have my loyalty."

"Then we are of an accord," she said.

They all got up to leave, but Murray stopped and looked back at Veronica.

"Thank you for giving me a new life. The chance to be with my wife and son." He turned a walked out of the room.

Veronica's eyes teared up, thinking how it must have hurt him to have sent his family away. She would make sure they have a happy life in Scotland.

She looked down at her stomach and felt a deep love for her baby. She needed to get everything taken care of, everything before the baby made its grand entry. The first thing was to get ahold of Audrey Herring and stop Ada before she did anything else. Then, hopefully, things would go according to plan.

*I finally see a happy future for myself,* Veronica thought as she sunk into the bed and went to sleep.

# CHAPTER
# TWENTY-ONE

Three things cannot be
long hidden, the sun,
the moon, and the truth.

Buddha

A month later, Veronica went to her father's home to talk to her mother. As she took off her cloak and gloves, Ellen walked up.

"Ronnie, I was not expecting you," she said as she hugged her.

"I need to speak to you."

"Okay, let us go into the dayroom. Charles has brought tea in."

"Yes, ma'am."

"So, what do you want to talk about?" Ellen asked as they sat on the couch.

"You know what happened at Lord Carlisle's ball?"

"Yes, Aaron informed me. I am so thankful we were warned. Did you find out whom Ada attained to carry out her plan?"

"Yes, but it is worthless information. It is her word against ours."

"I see."

"How long does everyone want to wait before we put an end to their actions?"

"We wanted to wait until you were pregnant, and no harm could come to you or your baby. But we do not know how Thomas will react to the truth."

"We know Agnes and Ada are going to deny all of it, and we only have Owen's word about their original plan," Veronica says worriedly.

"It is not just what they have done to you. We are exposing things from many years ago. Things that were done to a girl named Meredith. You know her as Audrey Herring."

"What happened to her?"

"Meredith was betrothed to Thomas, and Agnes wanted him. So, she paid someone to compromise her in the worse way."

"That is horrible. Do you have evidence?"

"Meredith found the person who ruined her. He is willing to tell all he knows."

"That is wonderful. With him and Owen, how can Lord Claridge not believe us?"

"I believe that he will. I do not know what he will do. We still need to wait till you are pregnant." Ellen noticed Veronica was smiling. "Are you pregnant?"

"Yes, almost three months."

"Your father is going to be so happy. He has been talking about grandbabies a lot lately."

"Let us wait to tell him."

"Why?"

"I hate to do this, but I might have to use it to keep Father from killing Owen." Veronica got quiet and looked down with a sad expression.

"What are you not telling me?"

"After the baby is born, I am divorcing Owen and moving to Blackthorn."

"Owen is just going to let his baby go?"

"I am not going to keep him away from his child. He can come to see it anytime, and I will come back to visit."

Ellen was quiet, thinking about what Veronica was planning. "If you think that is best, I will support you. But, as far as your father, I am not so sure he will like that you and the baby are so far away."

"I know. I will need your help with Father and Ellis."

"Oh, your brother might be harder to control after he finds out."

"This is such a mess. I had no idea things would turn out like this," said Veronica as she took a deep breath and let it out slowly.

"Oh, sweetie, neither did I." Ellen wrapped her arms around Veronica and held her close. She stayed in her arms, needing her mother's love.

Once they parted, Veronica stood up. "I want to go see Lucien for a bit."

"He will be so happy to see you," said Ellen as they walked toward the door.

"I need to send Meredith a message to see if she can meet with us this afternoon."

"That would be great if we could get this over with."

Later that evening, Veronica walked back into her home, where a worried Owen met her.

"Where have you been?" he asked, trying to keep his voice calm.

"With my mother."

"All day?"

"Yes. Is something wrong?"

"I was just worried about you. This was the first time you have been out since you were shot, and now that you are with child, I cannot help but worry something might happen to you."

She smiled and hugged him. It caught him by surprise, but then he wrapped his arms around her, holding her tight.

"It worries me so much. I will not lie; I am scared about whatever plot Ada is conjuring up now."

Veronica pulls back and looks at him. "Let us go to the office and talk," said Veronica as she held his hand, leading him into the office and toward the couch. "Mother and I met with Audrey this afternoon, and in two days, we will expose Agnes and Ada to Lord Claridge." Giving him a chance to handle the situation himself was only right.

"What if he does not want anything done?"

"Then Audrey will do what she has planned. That woman is brilliant. When she is finished, Agnes and Ada's reputation will be ruined."

"Will that not hurt Lord Claridge?"

"That is why we are giving him a chance to do what is right."

Owen looked down.

"I am sorry you have to be there to tell your part in all this."

"I know your family will hate me, especially Ellis. Losing his friendship will be really hard."

"I would like to say that will not happen, but I promise to talk to him."

"Thank you," he said, smiling.

"Tomorrow, I will go back to my father's. Mom and I will tell him everything because we think it is best if he has a day to calm down."

"You are probably right." Owen stood and held out his hand. "Let us get something to eat. It is late, and you need to rest."

She takes his hand, and he leads her out of the room.

The next day, Veronica and Ellen are silently sitting on the couch, watching Henry. They had finished telling him everything, and he had not moved or spoken.

"Do we need to get the doctor?" whispered Veronica, not taking her eyes off her father.

"I am going to kill him," Henry hollered as he stood up to leave.

Veronica ran and got in front of him. "You cannot."

"Veronica, do not try and stop me. He deserves it."

"I cannot let you hurt my baby's father."

"There is nothing you can say to make me change my...What did you say?"

Veronica smiled at her father. "I was wondering if you heard me."

"Am I going to be a grandfather?"

"Yes."

Henry pulled her to his chest in a tight hug. He pulled back and looked into her eyes. "You know, you don't need that man for a husband with your mother and me. I could still get rid of him," he said with a severe expression.

Veronica couldn't help but laugh. "Father, I love you, but no. Please do not hurt him. He has suffered quite a bit here lately. Finding out everything he believed in was a lie has been hard."

"After what he has done, it is not enough."

"Henry, your daughter has a point. You cannot kill the father of your grandchild. Let us let her handle Owen," Ellen said as she walked beside him. "We still need to discuss what is going to happen tomorrow."

"What is happening tomorrow?" asked Henry, looking at Ellen.

"You might want to sit back down," said Veronica.

"Oh, what now?" he said as he sat down.

They talked about how they would expose Agnes and Ada to Lord Claridge. Henry didn't say anything as he sat there, thinking about his friend.

"I hate what this is going to do to Thomas. But he needs to know what his wife and daughter have done."

"I was hoping you would send a message to him requesting a meeting tomorrow."

"Okay, I will," he replied, looking at Ellen.

"I need to go home. I am a little tired," said Veronica as she stood.

Ellen and Henry walked her to the door and hugged her before leaving.

"I am going to be a grandfather," he said with a big smile as he watched Veronica enter her carriage. Ellen decided not to say anything about Veronica moving to Scotland for now. Henry had enough to deal with for now. There was no need to worry him more.

"You are going to be an excellent grandfather," she said, kissing him on the cheek.

"Yes, I am," he replied as he turned to go to his office.

The day finally came when everyone would expose Agnes and Ada. Veronica and Owen arrived at the Aldridge home a little before ten. They saw Meredith sipping tea with Veronica's parents as they entered the room. Henry rose when he saw them walk in. The look on his face was anything but happy when he looked at Owen.

"My lord," Owen said as he slightly bowed.

"We will have a discussion in private when this is over."

After everyone was seated, Charles walked in. "Lord Hayworth and his son Oliver are here to see you."

"Send them in," he said as he greeted them.

Veronica looked at Ellen. "Why did he bring Oliver?"

"I do not know."

"Lord Aldridge."

"Lord Hayworth, come in. Good to see you," said Henry as he shook his hand. "You too, Oliver. Come in and take a seat."

Franklin Hayworth was a tall, slender man, very polite and refined. Once pleasantries were exchanged between everyone, they sat down.

"Lord and Lady Pierce, good to see you," said Oliver.

"Just Veronica, Oliver," she said, smiling.

"Veronica," replied Oliver, smiling back.

Oliver was tall like his father, more muscular with light brown hair and silver eyes. He was very handsome and was utterly in love with Hannah. If Ellis were not careful, he could lose her to that man.

Oliver leaned close to Veronica as Ellen and Meredith talked to Henry and Franklin in hushed voices. "Do you know why we are here?"

"I know why your father is here, but I am not sure why you are here."

Franklin cleared his throat, getting everyone's attention. "I brought my son with me here today because I want him to know how malicious and heartless people can be. There are times when people will use you and take advantage of those that are desperate. I hope when you hear my story, you can still call me father." His voice cracked a little, and everyone was moved by his words.

"I admire you for wanting to educate your son in this matter. You have fine qualities," said Meredith.

"I agree," said Henry as he patted Franklin's shoulder.

Charles walked back in. "Lord Claridge is here to see you, my lord."

"Show him in and shut the door," said Henry as he stood to greet Thomas.

"Hello, Henry," said Thomas as he shook his hand.

"Thomas, come sit down."

Thomas looked over everyone there and froze when he saw the woman sitting by Ellen. "Meredith," he whispered.

She got up and walked up to him. "Hello, Thomas."

Thomas grabbed her and pulled her into his arms. Then, realizing what he had done, he dropped his arms and stood back. "I am sorry. That was inappropriate."

"It is perfectly understandable. I was surprised seeing her, also," said Ellen.

"Please, come and sit. We have a lot to discuss," said Henry.

After everyone took their seat and pleasantries were exchanged, everyone grew quiet.

"Could someone tell me what's going on?" asked Thomas.

Ellen squeezed Meredith's hand, giving her the courage to speak.

"Thomas, there are things we need to tell you. It will be hard to hear but know everything we say will be the truth."

"The truth, about what?"

"I suppose we should start from the beginning," said Ellen as she looked at Franklin. "When I was a kid, my father squandered our family fortune. He stayed in gambling halls and brothels, never coming home. We were losing everything, leaving my mother and siblings on the streets. One day, a girl came to see me. She offered enough money to pay off our debt in exchange for my cooperation. I had never been in society. My father's actions left my family to be outcasts. I had no idea what what I was about to do would mean."

He paused and looked at Meredith before he continued. "One night, she came and took me to the Oprah house and hid me inside one of the rooms. There I would stay hidden until the unsuspecting victim showed up. I was in there for a while, then the door slowly opened, and a girl walked in. I hit her on the back of the head, knocking her out, and ripped her clothes, making it look like something bad had happened. Then, I waited until I saw two older women walking toward the room. I took off running, making as much noise as possible, getting their attention, and as she hoped, the women walked in and found the girl."

Meredith never looked up as he spoke.

Veronica looked at Oliver. He was breathing heavily with a look of rage on his face. He stood and hurriedly walked out of the room. Franklin went to stand up, but Veronica held out her hand to stop him.

"Let me go." She walked out, finding Aaron waiting outside.

"He went that way."

"Thank you."

Back inside the room, nobody spoke until Veronica shut the door.

"Who was it that hired you?" asked Henry, even though inside, he already knew.

Franklin looked at Thomas with sympathy in his eyes. "Agnes."

Rage filled Thomas, and he jumped up and headed for the door. However, Henry caught him before he got too far. "Thomas, calm down and get ahold of yourself."

"I always knew Agnes was not a prime and proper girl, but to know for definite what she is capable of..."

"I know this is hard, but it is going to get harder," said Ellen.

Thomas turns to look at her. "What could be harder? She took the love of my life away from me," he said as if defeated.

Tears formed in Meredith's eyes, and she quickly wiped the corners to keep them from falling.

Henry put his hand on his shoulder. "You need to sit down. There's more."

"More?" Thomas looked from Henry to the others as he sat down.

Veronica found Oliver standing in the garden with his eyes closed.

"Oliver," she said as she walked up beside him.

"How could he do something like that?" he said, not opening his eyes.

"Come over here and sit. There are some things you need to know." He looked down at her and slowly walked with her over to a bench. "Oliver, your father felt like he had no choice. He was desperate to protect his mother and siblings."

"No. What he did was unforgivable."

"Image your mother and sister on the streets. You know what more than likely would happen. It is not kind to people, especially women. What would you do to protect them?"

Oliver was quiet as he thought about what Veronica had said. "There is nothing I would not do to protect them."

"Your dad had no idea what all his actions would entail. Agnes told him it would only cause trouble with her betrothed. He did not understand how society worked. After a couple of years, your father looked into what had happened to her. When he found out, he looked for her. He was going to offer marriage to try and make amends."

"He was?"

"Oliver, your father is a good and noble man."

"You are right. He is."

"We need to get back. There is more that needs to be said about Agnes."

"Yes, let us go. I need to show my father that we are okay."

As they entered the room, they saw Thomas pacing and Henry trying to calm him down. Franklin looked at Oliver with hope, and Oliver smiled at him. You could see his eyes grow moist, and relief washed over his face.

Henry walked up to Veronica. "Owen just told Thomas about their plot to destroy you."

"Oh," Veronica replied, looking at Owen. He had his head down and eyes closed. She walked over and sat beside him, taking his hand in hers. Owen looked up at her, and she smiled. He took her hand and covered it with both of his.

"I am so sorry, Veronica," said Thomas, lowering his head.

"It was not your doing, Lord Claridge. You have nothing to be sorry for," she said. "Did you tell him about Randolph?" asked Veronica, looking at Owen.

"Randolph?" asked Henry.

"Malcolm Randolph?" asked Franklin.

"Do not tell me Agnes is in league with him?" said Thomas.

"No, Ada is," said Owen.

"Before we say anything further. Father, I need you to know I am okay. Owen, Aaron, and the guys protected me."

Henry sat down and looked at Veronica. "Tell me what happened?' he said in a very calm voice. Only Veronica and Ellen knew of the storm growing under Henry's calm demeanor.

Veronica looked at Ellen, unsure if she should continue.

Ellen decided she should start. "Meredith found out Ada was trying to enlist help to keep Veronica's child from inheriting Owen's title if she should have a boy."

"I do not understand. How would Ada keep the child from inheriting?" asked Thomas.

"If the child's father was in question," said Ellen, looking at Henry.

Henry stood slowly, evident of the rage boiling inside. "She tried to get someone to compromise Veronica?"

"Yes," said Ellen as she walked up to Henry, wrapping her arms around him and laying her head on his chest. He brought his arms up to hug her back as tears rolled down his face. "I have never regretted my fortune until this moment. My daughter has been a target of so many."

"Father, please do not blame yourself," said Veronica as she cried, seeing her father's pain. Henry looked over seeing his daughter crying. He walked toward her, and she stood, letting him wrap his arms around her.

"I love you, Father."

"Someone tell me how my daughter got tangled with Malcolm Randolph?"

Meredith took a deep breath and looked at Thomas. She hated having to tell him what his daughter was doing. "First, she tried to get Jeremy Hightower, but he refused. He even cut ties with her."

"Jeremy? He was one of the first to show interest in Ada when she first came out, but Agnes disapproved."

"They have secretly been meeting at White's Gentlemen's Club for over a year," said Owen.

"How do you know this? Could it be only a rumor?" asked Thomas, hoping it wasn't as bad as it sounded.

"It is more than a rumor. I am so sorry," said Meredith.

Thomas's shoulders slumped as his head lowered. "My daughter," he said as tears fell from his eyes. Everyone was quiet as they felt his pain. To find out one's child would do something so revolting... "So, she convinced Randolph to attack Veronica?" he said as he wiped the tears off his face.

"Malcolm was not stupid enough to do it himself, so he made one of his footmen. A young man just sixteen who was captured and admitted everything."

"So, there was a witness?" asked Henry.

"It is a footmen's word against a Randolph's," said Veronica.

"Besides, we all know Randolph will kill him," said Franklin.

"I am sure he thinks we did that for him. Right now, I am more worried about what plan Ada will come up with next," said Owen.

"You have told me about this to give me a chance to stop them. I know Henry could easily take action, but he has not."

"We have been friends for a long time. We wanted to give you a chance to do something about this, but I must warn you that a simple scolding will not deter them, nor will it satisfy my need for revenge," said Henry.

"I think my son and I will take our leave. There will be things you will need to discuss, and I need to talk with my son," said Franklin as he stood. Oliver stood and followed his father out of the room with Meredith not far behind.

"Franklin," she said as they reached the front door. "Thank you for doing this. I know it was hard for you."

"I can never do enough to make up for the pain I caused you."

"It is over now, and I shall never speak of this again."

"Thank you, Lady Ferguson," he said with a slight bow, then left for their carriage.

She returned to the room, feeling a heavy weight had been lifted off her. She saw Thomas sitting, looking lost.

Ellen walked over and sat beside him. "I have a room already prepared for you. Right now, you must rest and think about what you will do."

"You are right. I do need time to think. I would very much like to accept the offer," he said as he rose.

Henry walked up to him. "If you do not feel like coming down for supper, we will send it up to your room. If you need someone to talk to, I am here."

"Thank you, Henry."

"Charles, show Lord Claridge to his room," said Ellen.

Before Thomas left the room, he stopped and looked at Meredith longingly, then continued out the door.

"We are heading home. I will come by tomorrow," said Veronica as she and Owen stood to leave.

"I have a question. Veronica, where did you find your servants?" asked Meredith.

Veronica and Owen tensed as they looked at her.

"What do you mean?" asked Veronica, trying to sound confused.

"I was able to put a spy, or at least, get information everywhere except your house. When everyone went to your wedding, I had a girl befriend one of your stable boys. He became very smitten with the girl and would talk about everything except you. All servants know each other. Some meet at social functions, some when shopping. They are the best at acquiring information, but nobody knows your servants. They have seen them and even tried to start conversations, but they are tight-lipped. I have never seen servants as loyal as yours. Your stable boy said he owed you his life."

"I do not know what to say. I am very good to my servants."

Henry could tell Veronica was nervous. He looked and saw Aaron in the doorway. "Aaron, come in here."

Aaron stepped into the office, looking at only Henry. Veronica knew he was trying to act as if everything was fine.

"Do you know anything about Veronica's servants?"

"Sir? I am not sure what you are asking?"

"Where did Veronica get her servants?" The way Aaron was acting told Henry something was going on. Aaron was quiet and looked toward Veronica, giving her a chance to speak. She knew he was not going to lie to Henry.

"I found my servants," she said.

"What do you mean by found?"

"Okay, just know I always had one or two men around for protection."

"Aaron, you had better tell me because my daughter will be sure to leave out things that will upset me."

"She rescued them, sir."

"Excuse me? What do you mean by rescued?"

"Father, I am right here."

"Are you going to tell me everything? Because you know I will not stop until I find out."

"Yes."

"Okay, Aaron, you can go."

As he left, he gave a thank-you look to Veronica.

"Everybody better sit back down. This will take a while."

Everyone was stunned after Veronica told them everything she had done to help others.

"And you let her do this?" Henry said to Owen.

"I did not even know about it until the night she..." Owen paused, realizing what he was about to say.

"The night she what?"

Owen looked at Veronica, knowing he just made things worse.

"The night I was shot," she whispered.

Ellen gasped and covered her mouth with her hand. Henry quickly stood and grabbed Veronica by the arms, pulling her up. Owen jumped up, not knowing what Henry was going to do.

He looked at his daughter, then pulled her to his chest, hugging her. "Please, stop. Just stop," Henry said as he wept. Veronica held her dad as tears fell from her eyes. She never thought about her actions causing her father so much pain.

"Father, I promise you I am no longer putting myself in harm's way." He released her and stepped back.

"How can I believe you? It seems to be in your blood to do dangerous things."

"Because I am going to be a mother. I will not risk my baby's life."

"Will that truly settle you down?

"Yes," she said smiling.


On the way home, Owen looked at Veronica, smiling.

"What are you smiling about?"

"You caused your father to forget about the discussion we were supposed to have. I feel like I owe you my life."

"Oh, do not worry, he will get to you eventually," she said, smiling back.

"I am sure he will. I am relieved it is out in the open. What do you think Lord Claridge is going to do?"

"I do not know. What do you do when you have so many years with someone, and you find out what a horrible person they are? My heart goes out to him, but I cannot feel sympathy for Agnes and Ada. No matter what he does to them," said Veronica looking out the window.

"Do you think that makes you a bad person?"

"Does it?"

"No, Veronica. After everything they have done and tried to do to you, you did not ask your father to end them. Most people with that kind of power at their disposal would have."

"It never occurred to me to have my dad do that."

"And that is what makes you a good person."

"Thank you. I feel better."

"You are welcome."

"You never did tell me what your parents said about the baby?" Veronica asked.

"I have not told them," he said looking away.

"Why?"

"I have not been back there since my father found out what I did."

"Owen, you need to try and repair things with your family."

"I do not know how. My father was so angry and disappointed with me. I do not think he will ever forgive me."

Veronica thought for a second. "I am going to send an invite for supper tomorrow night. I need to talk to Dinah anyway, and if we show them that we are agreeable with each other, then we will surprise them with the news of our baby. What do you think?"

"I would like that. You are incredible."

"I know," she said, looking out the window, grinning.

He looked at Veronica, wishing he had gotten to know her before tangling with someone like Ada.


Back at the Aldridge home, Thomas sat by the fire in a daze, thinking about everything he had learned. Agnes had robbed him of a life with Meredith.

When supper was ready, Henry had a servant take enough for two people, knowing Thomas wasn't ready to come out. When Thomas opened the door, he was surprised to see so much food.

"Would you mind if I join you for supper?"

"Yes, please. I could use some advice," Thomas said, stepping aside to let in the servant and Henry.

The rest of the evening, they sat and talked.

"I guess I should get going," said Thomas as he stood.

"No, spend the night. I have already sent a message that you had business and will return tomorrow. I would feel better if you stayed, and in the morning, you can have everything you need prepared and ready before you go home. You cannot give Agnes any time to develop a countermove."

"You are correct. Thank you, Henry. You have been a good friend."

"I will always be here if you need me," said Henry as he left the room.

Thomas sat by the fire for a bit longer, going over their plan. He finally went to bed, knowing he would need his wits about him for the next day as he dealt with Agnes.

# CHAPTER TWENTY

Many things in life are
not what they seem.
The worst things in
life never are.

Jim Butcher

The following morning, Thomas comes down for breakfast with a new determination. After bidding farewell to Henry and Ellen, he went to his solicitors to prepare the documents he would need. Once arriving home, he went to his office after sending the butler to get Agnes.

"Hello, Thomas. When did you get home?"

"Just now. I need you to sign these documents."

"What documents?"

"This is a property in Sussex that I recently purchased. I am putting it in your name."

"Really? You are giving me property? Why?"

"Since I do not have a son, I want to make sure you and Ada have something when I am gone." He hated to act as if he cared, but it was the only way to get her to sign all the papers he needed.

She started signing documents without even reading them. She knew he was acting strange, but she only thought of how jealous all the other women would be of her.

Once signed, Thomas called for a footman to come and take the forms immediately to parliament.

"Why did you send the property title to parliament and not to the solicitor?"

"Oh, the property deed will go to the solicitor. It was the divorce papers that went to parliament."

"What divorce?"

"We are divorcing, and you will need to go and pack your things. I want you out of this house by this afternoon." Thomas was very calm as he spoke to Agnes.

She stood there, not knowing what had just happened. "What is going on? I do not understand?"

"Well, let me make it clear. I am divorcing you."

"Why would you do this?"

"Maybe because I found out what a despicable person you are. You are a horrible, vile creature."

"How dare you speak to me like that?" she yelled.

"I will speak to you any way I choose after what I found out."

"What are you saying? What have I done?"

"You do not know? I guess you have done so much, I will have to remind you. Franklin Hayworth."

Agnes grew pale and sat down.

"I see you remember him. How could you do something like that? You took the woman I loved away from me."

"I loved you too. She did not deserve you. Have I not been a good wife to you?"

"Have you? Or have you used your status to hurt anyone that got in your way?"

"I have not hurt anyone. I did what I had to do." Agnes was too proud to admit any wrongdoing.

"Oh. What about Veronica Aldridge?"

"What about her?" she said, acting like she was confused.

"I know Agnes. I know everything. But do you know what our daughter has been doing at White's club?"

"White's?"

"Did you know she has been meeting with Jeremy Hightower?"

"She thought he didn't know everything, or she would be hauled off to prison or dead. You taught her well. She has perfected being a whore."

Agnes slapped his face.

"That is a lie. She would never do that."

Thomas laughed, and Agnes thought he had gone mad. "Oh, Agnes, something you did not know. Your daughter has been meeting Jeremy Hightower for over a year, and several know about Malcolm. She is ruined, and there is nothing you can do about it. Once our divorce circulates, you will be too."

"You cannot do this."

"I already have, but do not worry. I did put a property in your name. So, you will not be living on the streets. But do not think for one second you will be living in extravagance. It is a small house. You will not have any servants to push around and mistreat. I will supply you with enough food for a short time until you find employment and get a garden growing," said Thomas as he sat behind his desk, going through some papers.

"A garden? Do you mean I am going to live in squaller?"

"Your fortunate I do not throw you out on your arse. So, you can either go there or back to your parents. But I do not think they will welcome you once they know about the divorce."

"I am not going anywhere," she said determinedly.

"You can either go willingly, or I will have you dragged out of here. Imagine the gossip that would cause." Thomas laughed.

"You would not dare," she yelled.

The door opened, and Ada walked in. "What is going on? Why are you yelling at each other?"

"There you are, right on time. Your mother is moving out. If you want to stay here, you will do what I say."

"What?! Mother, what is he talking about?"

"He knows Ada. He is divorcing me, and I have to leave."

She let tears fall from her eyes, thinking Ada would get her father to change his mind.

"Dad, you cannot do this. You and Mother have been together for a long time. Please do not do this," she pleads to him softly.

"Is this how you act to get all those men in bed?"

Ada stepped back as if he had hit her. "What are you talking about?"

"I know, Ada. I know about Jeremy, and oh god, let us not forget about Malcolm Randolph." Ada grew pale and looked at her mother.

"This is how things are. Your mother and I are divorcing. She will be leaving to live in Essex today. If you stay, you will do as I say, go where I say, and marry whom I say. If anyone still wants you after it gets out what you have done. Oh, and if either one of you tries to hurt Veronica again, I will not be able to stop Henry from ending you."

Ada shrinks down in a chair. She looks at her mother, hoping she will know what to do. "Mother?"

"Ada, you must do what your father tells you. I will always love you, but now because of my decisions, things will be different. Stay strong and try to maintain a proper image. Things might be tough, but you will be okay," said Agnes as she hugged Ada.

Thomas sat and watched, trying to feel something other than disgust but couldn't. They had done so much, he couldn't feel any compassion.

"I want you out by this afternoon. Ada, you must stay home until I figure out what to do with you." He got up and walked out of the office.

"Mom, what do I do?"

"Try to get ahold of Owen and see if he knows anything. That might be our only hope."

Later that evening, after Agnes left for her exile, Thomas left to handle some business, and Ada has an opportunity to sneak out to find Owen.

Callum, Ann, and Dinah exited their carriage, excited and nervous about Veronica's invitation. Once they entered, James showed them into the sitting room. It didn't take long for the door to open, and Veronica walked in, smiling.

"Hello, everyone. Thank you for coming on short notice."

Callum got up and walked over and hugged her. "I am so sorry for what my family has done."

"That is in the past. Owen and I have agreed, and we are quite happy with everything," she said, smiling at him.

"Good, I am glad."

Ann walked over with her head lowered. "Can you ever forgive me?"

"I have come to understand that when people are desperate, they are vulnerable, and others can take advantage of it. So yes, I can forgive you."

Ann looked up at her and was surprised at how pretty she looked. Veronica's hair was pulled back, tied with peached colored ribbons leaving the back in large curls. Her dress was plain and modest, but the peach color made her skin look bright and glow.

"Thank you, sweet girl."

Veronica looked over at Dinah and saw her sitting, looking at the floor. She walked over and stood in front of her. "Do I not get a hug?"

Dinah raised her head and looked at Veronica. She stood up with tears in her eyes.

Reaching out, they embraced as tears rolled down her face. "I am so sorry, Veronica."

Veronica pulled back and looked at her. "Dinah, you have always been my friend, and you still are. I understand you were in the middle. Me on one end, your family on the other. Nobody should have to go through that," she said as she wiped Dinah's tears.

"I have missed you," said Dinah.

"I missed you too."

The door opened, and Owen walked in. He walked to his father and held out his hand. Callum looked at Owen's hand and then back up. He grabbed Owen and pulled him in for a hug, surprising him.

Veronica and Dinah stood there and watched with smiles on their faces.

"Dinner is served," said James.

Halfway through the meal, they heard someone yelling outside the door.

"I need to see Owen. NOW! Move out of my way, your big arse."

Everyone froze. Forks in midair, wine glasses stuck to lips.

Slowly Veronica and Owen turned to look at each other.

"For all that is holy, why now?" Owen whispered to himself.

"Everyone, please excuse us while we handle this," said Veronica as she and Owen left the table.

Owen opened the door and saw Ian and Michael blocking Ada. Michael tried hard not to laugh as Ada hit Ian in the chest with her fist. Ian had a smirk on his face, watching that little girl try to beat him up.

"ENOUGH!" hollered Owen.

Ada stopped and looked around Ian.

They look at Veronica, and she waved for them to let her by.

"Oh, Owen," Ada says as she ran to him, wrapping her arms around his waist. "You have to help me."

"Help you?" said Owen as he removed her arms from around him. "Why would I help you? I want nothing to do with you. Now leave, and never come around my family or me again." He then turned and walked back inside the dining room.

Ada watched him walk off, knowing she no longer had any control over him. "This is all your fault," she said, looking at Veronica.

"Ada, do you know why I try to be nice to people? Let me tell you. I figured out a long time ago that everyone, and I mean everyone, eventually gets their comeuppance. Nobody forced you to do the things you have done, and if you are not careful, you will lose your chance at a good life."

Ada lowered her head. Veronica turned around to left but stopped when she heard Ada in a low voice say, "I am scared."

Veronica turned around, looked at her, and saw tears running down her face. She walked over and stood in front of her.

"I have lost everything. My mother is gone, and my father hates me."

"Your father does not hate you. He loves you."

"Not anymore."

"Ada, I watched your father cry over you. That man loves you and has given you a chance to do right."

"How do you know that?" she said, crying harder.

Veronica wrapped her arms around Ada, letting her cry on her shoulder.

"Because he did not send you away with your mother. If he hated you, he would not have allowed you to stay."

Ada stepped back, wiping her face. "You believe that?"

"Yes. Now go home and talk to him. Be honest and make amends. He loves you, Ada." Veronica gave Ada a second to get ahold of her emotions. "Did you come in a carriage?"

"No, I grabbed a coach."

"Ian, bring around a carriage."

"It is already out front," said Ian.

"Good. Make sure she gets home safely."

Ada turned to follow Ian out when she stopped. "Veronica?" she said, not turning around.

"Yes."

"I am sorry," she said, then walked out.

After walking back and sitting down at the table, she saw everyone staring at her.

"You are a good person, Veronica Pierce," said Callum.

"I honestly believe that without her mother around, Ada could be a better person."

"You might be right," said Dinah.

"If she truly makes an attempt, I will not shun her," said Veronica.

"Now, I would like to make a toast," said Owen as he raised his glass. Everyone held up their glasses, looking toward him. "To my family that is here and the little one yet to come," he said, smiling.

"Are you saying Veronica is pregnant?" asked Ann.

"Yes, we are going to have a baby in about seven months."

Dinah jumped up and ran to Veronica as she stood, hugging her.

Callum walked to Owen and shook his hand. "Congratulations, son."

"Thank you, grandpa."

"Grandpa. I like the sound of that."

Ann walked over to Veronica. Dinah stepped back and looked at her mother. "Veronica, I am so happy. You are going to be a great mother."

"Thank you," said Veronica as she hugged Ann.

"This calls for a celebration. More wine, but not for you," said Callum, causing Veronica to laugh.

Owen looked over at her and mouthed, 'thank you.'

A couple of months passed, and the knowledge about the divorce didn't take long to affect Ada. But that wasn't the catalyst that ruined her reputation. It was the rumor of her relationship with Malcolm Randolph. There were no invitations to social functions, and all her so-called friends refused even to see her. However, she did work hard to repair her relationship with her father. They became closer than they had ever been, making Ada see things in a different light. She admitted everything she had done and showed Thomas she was trying to improve.

Veronica, Hannah, and Dinah were at the dressmaker's shop getting Veronica some new dresses made for her growing stomach and ever-so-enlarged breast. As they were leaving, Ada walked in. She looked down, not sure if she should try to speak.

"Hello, Ada," said Veronica.

"Hello," she replied, not looking up. She wasn't sure how to react to Veronica being friendly.

"How have you been?" Veronica was shocked at how Ada was acting.

"Okay, thank you for asking."

Hannah and Dinah were also shocked at how Ada was acting. She was no longer spiteful and proud.

"Well, have a good day," said Veronica as she walked past, not wanting to make her any more uncomfortable than she already seemed.

"Thank you. You as well."

Veronica then noticed Ada's old friends in the corner, laughing and pointing at Ada. She looked back and saw Ada walking with her head down.

*This will not do,* Veronica thought. "Ada," she raised her voice to get everyone's attention.

Ada turned around. "Yes?'

"Would you like to meet for tea one day this week?"

"Yes, I would like that," she said with a smile.

"Then I will be in touch," said Veronica as she left.

The girls stopped their laughter and went about their own business, leaving Ada alone. Since Agnes was gone, Veronica, Hannah, and Dinah's mothers had become more of a lead in the ton, and nobody wanted to offend them.

After they sat inside the carriage, Hannah and Dinah stared at her. "What?"

"Why are you being friendly to her?" asked Hannah.

"Ada has been trying to turn her life around. Dad has been keeping in touch with her father. She admitted to everything she had done. I do not want to be why she cannot stay on a better path. I hope you both can forgive her and be a friend to her after I am gone. Everyone deserves a second chance."

"You plan on still leaving after the baby is born?" asked Hannah.

"What do you mean leaving?" asked Dinah.

"I am going on with the plan to get a divorce."

"But why? I thought you and Owen were getting along?"

"We agreed on a compromise. So, I am taking the baby and moving to my home in Scotland. Do not worry. I will not keep Owen or your family away from the baby. I would not do that."

Dinah didn't say anything. She was surprised that things would turn out like that.

"Dinah, are you okay?" asked Veronica.

"I am just surprised. I thought you and Owen would try to have a family. I will miss you."

"I will come back to visit, and I expect both of you to come to see me."

"Of course we will," said Hannah.

"Do my mother and father know?" asked Dinah.

"I do not want them to know. Owen and your father have just repaired their relationship. I do not want any problems between them. So, please, do not say anything right now."

"All right."

That evening Veronica was sitting by the fire when Owen returned home. He stood in the doorway and watched her as she knitted. She looked up and saw him standing there.

"How long have you been there?"

"Not long," he said as he walked in and sat in a chair beside her.

She got a strange look on her face and grabbed his hand, putting it on her belly. "Do you feel that?"

He looks at his hand as a smile grows on his face.

"That is a kick. Oh, it is very active today," she said as a wave went across her stomach.

Owen watched in awe as his baby seemed to be stretching inside her belly. "Does it hurt?"

"Sometimes, but mainly it just feels strange."

"I cannot wait to see him," said Owen.

"You think it is a boy?"

"I just say him. If it is a girl, I will spoil her rotten."

"You and our parents. Did you know your father and mine have Ian sending them updates on my condition?" she said, laughing.

"I am not surprised," he said, laughing with her.

They sat and talked the rest of the evening. That had become a typical day between them. To everyone, they would seem to be a happy family. Nobody could see the pain in Veronica's heart.

# CHAPTER
# TWENTY-THREE

The two most important warriors
are patience and time.

Leo Tolstoy

One morning Lydia was helping Veronica get dressed when she noticed a big smile on Lydia's face.

"Why are you so happy this morning?

"Adrian asked me to marry him last night."

"Oh, Lydia, congratulations," said Veronica as she hugged her. "This is fantastic. Have you set a date? You know I am going to give you a large wedding."

"That is not a good idea. Remember, we are both hiding."

"I know," Veronica said, smiling.

Lydia watched Veronica, knowing she was up to something.

That afternoon, Veronica called Adrian and Lydia into the office. When they entered, they saw Owen sitting behind the desk and Veronica sitting in a chair.

"Come in, take a seat," said Owen. "Would you like to start?" he asked Veronica.

"A while back, I came across a gentleman that had fallen on hard times. Or that was what he said. But unfortunately, the truth was that his son squandered their fortune. So, I bought the estate and set them up so they could spend their remaining days in peace. I have been waiting for you to ask Lydia to marry you. I thought I was going to have to threaten you."

"She was getting impatient," said Owen.

Everyone laughed except Veronica. She looked at them as if they had lost their minds, making them laugh hard.

"I am trying to say we want to give you and Lydia the estate."

Adrian and Lydia sat there with their mouths open, stunned.

"It's not a large estate, but it does have several tenant homes you will have to repair and get rented. But, with some hard work, you could have a good income. And also, the current doctor wants to retire," said Owen.

"What estate is it?" asked Lydia.

"In New Castleton," said Veronica.

"Not Lord Chambers?" asked Adrian.

"Yes, you know him?" asked Owen.

"No, I went to school with his son. A complete idiot. All he wanted to do was drink port and tupp women. Sorry for my language," said Adrian. He badly wanted to accept the offer and give Lydia a good home and her station back, but there was one problem.

"You are worried about your brother?" asked Veronica.

"Yes."

"We have thought about that also. The estate is smaller than the one he now has, so there should be no jealousy, and Owen and I will have a meeting with him. We have also come up with stories to explain both your re-entries into society and how you met. I promise that if you except, things will go smoothly. We can step out and let you two talk, if you need time?"

Adrian and Lydia looked at each other.

"I will go with you no matter what you choose," said Lydia smiling.

"I accept, but on two conditions. First, I want to be there when you talk to my brother."

"Of course, and the other?" asked Owen.

"I want to pay you back for the estate."

"How about we talk about investing together?" asked Veronica as she rose slowly, using the desk as leverage due to her protruding belly.

"That sounds wonderful," said Adrian as he stood and shook Owen's hand.

"I cannot take any of the credit. It was Veronica's idea."

"I am so happy. You will be running your own home. Also, New Castleton is on the Scotland border," Veronica said to Lydia as she hugged her.

"We can visit each other as often as we want. Thank you, Veronica," said Lydia.

"Now you can have that big wedding I want," said Veronica as she left the room, leaving everyone shaking their heads.

The next morning, Veronica came down the stairs, seeing Owen talking to Ian and Michael.

"Where are you going this morning?" asked Owen.

"How do you know I am going somewhere?"

"You always wear that dress when you go out. You should go and have more dresses made if you do not have any that fit."

Ian and Michael moved around behind Veronica as they listened to what Owen was saying.

"What are you trying to say?" asked Veronica, crossing her arms in front of her.

Ian and Michael start shaking their heads, trying to warn him not to say anything more. They had already witnessed how sensitive she was about getting big.

Seeing their warning, he smiled. "I want you to enjoy this time and go shopping. Once the baby gets here, you will not have much time to enjoy yourself." He holds his breath, hoping he covers well.

"Aaron sent word Ellis is at Father's. I am tired of him ignoring us, so that is where I am going," she said as he moved past him. "Oh, by the way, Ian, Michael, I will get you back for warning him," she said with a big smile as she entered the dining room for breakfast.

They hurriedly followed her, denying they had done anything.

Owen couldn't help but laugh at how a little woman could make two grown men squirm.


When Veronica arrived at her father's home, Charles informed her Ellis was in the office with her parents. She walked to the door but stopped when she heard their conversation.

"Ellis, you cannot keep avoiding them," said Henry.

"Dad, I cannot go over there. All I want to do is kill him for what he did."

"Can you not just let it lie? Your sister is what is important, not Owen. She misses you and does not need the added stress," said Ellen.

"I know, Mother. I do not know what to do."

She opened the door and saw her brother looking out the window. "I guess you can keep acting like you do not have a sister," Veronica said as tears rolled down her face.

Everyone was surprised to see her. Ellis saw his sister standing there crying and walked over. She looked at him, and he wrapped his arms around her. "I am so sorry," he said, causing her to break down and cry harder.

Suddenly he jumped back and looked down at her belly.

"I guess the baby is mad at you, too," she said as she placed her hand on her stomach. "It kicked him," she said, looking at her parents.

"Can I touch?" asked Ellis.

Veronica placed his hand on her stomach, and his eyes grew big when something seemed to push against his palm.

"I think that is a hand. It must want to hold yours," she said, smiling.

"I am so sorry I have not come around," said Ellis, feeling guilty for not visiting his sister.

"I know how stubborn you are and how you always stay away from things that upset you, but I need you around."

"Why do we not go and give them some time to talk?" said Henry as he walked toward Ellen, taking her hand and leaving.

"It is strange not to see Ailbert anymore," said Veronica as she sat on the couch. Ellis took a seat across from her.

"Yes, I guess it was true he only stayed because of us. I am glad he is back in Scotland. I believe he missed his brother more than he would ever admit."

"I missed mine too."

"I am sorry, Ronnie. For everything," he said, looking down.

"What are you talking about?"

"I let you marry him."

"You blame yourself?"

"Yes, I trusted him. I was happy you married him, for God's sake." Ellis stood, angry, and walked to the window.

"How could you have known? Nobody knew what Agnes was up to."

"I knew how much he loved Ada. I should have known he would not have given up that easy," said Ellis, running his hand through his hair.

Veronica got up and walked beside him, looking out the window. "I am to blame for this. My instincts told me someone was forcing Owen to marry me. But everyone was so worried about me finding a husband, I ignored everything in me warning me."

Ellis turned towards her, seeing her sad.

"Ellis, I have a huge favor to ask you," she said, looking out the window.

"Do not ask me to overlook what he has done."

"I need to tell you my plan before you refuse," she said as she returned to the couch.

He followed and sat back across from her.

"Once the baby is born and old enough to travel, I am taking it and moving to Scotland."

"What about Owen?"

"I am divorcing him."

"You are taking the baby and just leaving?"

"I will not keep him from the baby. He can come and see it anytime he wants, and I will be back to visit."

"And Owen is okay with this?"

"We had an agreement in the beginning when I first found out about Agnes's plan, but that was before Ada was exposed."

"You think Owen has changed his mind?"

"He has been a perfect husband," she said, looking off in deep thought.

"Has he fallen in love with you?"

"I think he has fallen in love with the thought of a family. He was devastated about Ada, and I think he needs something to love."

"And you are not willing to try? Why?"

"I do not know why. My baby would do much better with a whole family."

"But? You cannot forgive him?"

"No, it is nothing like that. I have forgiven him and know he will be an incredible father. I just want to go to the castle and live my life there with my baby. I want to be away from London and society. Oh, and Father does not know yet, so do not say anything. Okay?"

"What do you think he is going to say?" said Ellis as he rubbed his forehead.

"I do not think he will be happy."

"Okay, well, what is the big favor?"

"I do not know how Owen will be when I leave. I am not asking you to be his friend. I need someone who knows him to make sure my baby's father will be around. I could not take it if something were to happen to him."

"Okay, I see what you are asking for. I will be sure and check on him for my little niece or nephew," Ellis said, smiling.

"Thank you," she said, smiling back.

"Let us go have lunch with Mother and Father," he said, holding out his hand to help her up.

Out in Sussex, the first few months were hell for Agnes. She had no maids or any help whatsoever. The only person she saw was the man that brought her supplies, but she knew that would soon end. She constantly tried to think of ways to get back to society and maybe find another husband to support her, but nobody was willing to help.

Eventually, she went into the small town close to her home to check things out. Not wanting any attention, she wore a commoner's dress and rode her horse with no saddle. Agnes was glad her father taught her to ride when she was young.

Going up and down the town, looking at all the shops and businesses, she decided it might be good to find work until Ada could come and get her. She hadn't heard from her yet but knew she would eventually.

Tired from walking, she went into a tavern and ordered food and tea. The place was busy, and she noticed the woman waiting on tables looked worn out.

"Does this place need any help?"

"Yes, our cook quit."

"I can cook, and I need a job."

"You are the person that moved in the house down the north road?"

"Yes," Agnes replied, smiling.

"I can give you a try. When can you start?"

"How about after I finish eating?"

"Sounds good," said the woman, leaving Agnes to wait on another customer.

Even though Agnes's father was a wealthy baron, her mother taught her how to cook and clean. She didn't want her daughter to grow up spoiled, which made her resent her mother until that moment.

It had been years since she had cooked, but it didn't take long for it all to come back to her.

Late that evening, she finally made it home and soaked in her bath. After finishing up and getting a fire started, she curled up on her couch with one of the few books Thomas let her bring when she heard a knock at the door. Surprised and nervous, she went to the window and saw a carriage and a woman at the front door. Thinking it must be a friend of hers that had come to save her, she ran and opened the door.

The woman slowly lowered the hood of her cloak, revealing her face. Agnes stood in shock, never expecting to see that person ever in her life.

"Hello, Agnes," said Meredith, smiling.

"What are you doing here?"

"I would like to speak to you."

"I have nothing to say to you," said Agnes as she tried to shut the door.

Meredith grabbed the door before she could close it. "You will want to hear what I have to say, or I could go to the magistrate with what I know, and they will definitely come to talk to you."

"What are you talking about?"

"Leah," was all Meredith said to stun Agnes enough for her to push the door back open and walk on in.

"Get out of my house," Agnes said, standing at the door as Meredith made her way to a chair beside the fire.

"Do you not want to know what I learned?" she said as she sat down.

Agnes closed the door, walked over, and sat on the couch. "Say what you need to, then leave."

"When I was snooping around, I came across some fascinating information."

"It was you that ruined my marriage."

"I just paid back the favor you did me all those years ago."

"You have seen your handy work, so you can leave now."

"Oh, that is not why I am here. I came to tell you that if you try to hurt anybody else, I will see you hanged for the murder of Leah Aldridge."

Agnes sat there, not moving. *There is no way she knows that,* thought Agnes. "I have no idea what you are talking about."

"Then let me remind you. You had a maid from your house deliver poison to a maid that worked for Leah. The poor girl did not know it was going to kill her. She was friends with your maid and was convinced it would help Leah. After she died, the maid quit, and a month later, her body was found floating in the Thames."

"That is an interesting story, but none of it is true," said Agnes as she stared at the fire.

"Do you not want to know how I found out?" Meredith was quiet, waiting for Agnes to respond, but not a word was spoken. "I always had my suspicions about Leah's death, but when I found out she was helping Ellen in trying to find the person who hurt me, I knew. Leah was clever, more intelligent than all of us. She had you figured it out from the beginning. Warned us to stay away from you, but we did not listen. So instead, we played right into your hands."

Agnes never moved as Meredith talked. Instead, she just stared at the fire as if she was far away in her thoughts.

"After I discovered what happened to the maid, I tracked down her parents. Believe it or not, the girl wrote a confession in case something happened to her, but her parents were so afraid they would be blamed, they kept it to themselves. But I knew I needed more evidence than a letter. And then I got lucky when Thomas sent you away.

"You see, you got rid of the maid at Henry's but did not do anything to yours. I am guessing you thought you were so feared, nobody would betray you. Your maid confirmed it all, but she will stay quiet as long as I tell her to." Meredith stopped talking and started watching the fire as she thought about her friend that had lost her life trying to help her. She didn't realize tears had been rolling down her face as she talked.

Agnes finally turned and looked at Meredith. "What now?"

"All I want you to do is stay here and never return to London. I will never reveal what I know as long as you never hurt anyone again, especially Veronica. She has suffered enough because of you, and so has your daughter."

"What about Ada?"

"She has had a rough time being ostracized by society, but she has repaired her relationship with her father, and Henry has offered to help Thomas in finding a suitable match for her. So, coming back would only hurt her." Meredith stood. "If you love your daughter, stay away from her and let her have a good life."

Before Meredith reached the door, she heard Agnes in a low voice, "I never meant to kill her."

Meredith stopped for a second but continued out the door without a reply.

Agnes continued to stare at the fire as tears roll down her face. She did love her daughter, and if staying away was what it took to give Ada a good life, then that was what she would do.

After crying for a while, she got up and went to bed, accepting her life as it is now.

# CHAPTER
## TWENTY-FOUR

Forgiveness is a funny thing.
It warms the heart and
cools the sting.

William Arther Ward

I n Scotland, Sean was visiting Seinaid and Kieran. While sitting on the floor playing with Seinaid and Liam's five-month-old son, Acair, he listened to them talking about Veronica.

"She will be moving here after her bairn is born."

"What? Why are they moving here?" asked Sean.

"Not they, just Ronnie and the bairn," said Seinaid.

"I do not understand. What has happened?"

"She did not go into detail. All she wrote is they are getting a divorce after the bairn gets here."

"If it is true, this could be your chance," said Kieran.

"I do not know what you are talking about," said Sean, paying attention to little Acair.

"Sean, we know you still care about her," said Kieran.

"That was a long time ago," he replied, not looking away from the baby.

Seinaid and Kieran looked at each other, knowing Sean had loved Veronica since they were kids and still did. Seinaid started thinking that if Veronica did move there after her divorce, maybe she could help put them together.

*This will be fun.* She smiles as she watches Sean play with her son.

Back in London, dinner was being served to a full table. Owen sat at the head with Veronica to his right. Sitting beside her was her father and mother. To Owen's left were his father and mother. Lydia and Adrian also joined them. They had informed everyone of Adrian's new estate and return to public life. So, it was decided they should get used to their station again. They had come for a visit, and to Veronica's discomfort, they decided to stay.

"Excuse me," Veronica said as she stood. Everyone grew quiet as they watched her leave the table. Then, before anyone could ask, she turned around before she reached the door. "I need to relieve myself, and no, I do not need any help." She then turned around and left.

After a couple of minutes, Lydia noticed the room got quiet. She looked up and saw everyone staring at her.

"I will go check on her," she said as she put her fork down and stood.

"I will go with you," said Dinah.

They found Veronica sitting on the stairs.

"Why are you here?" asked Dinah.

"I just needed some alone time. I know they are concerned, but I feel confined. Father even made me and Owen start sharing a room in case something happened during the night."

Lydia and Dinah tried not to laugh at Veronica sulking because they knew she was miserable.

"I guess we had better get back before they send the calvary," said Veronica. So, Lydia and Dinah started walking back but stopped when they realize Veronica had not gotten up.

They walked back to her and noticed she was crying.

"What is wrong?" asked Lydia.

"I cannot get up," she said, wiping her eyes.

"Oh, do not cry," said Dinah as she and Lydia took Veronica's arms and helped her up.

They started walking toward the dining room but stopped again, noticing Veronica was not moving anymore. Looking at her, they saw a strange look on her face.

"Veronica?" said Lydia, starting to worry.

"I think my water broke," said Veronica as she looked down, seeing liquid running out from under her dress. Then she grabbed her stomach as she felt a slight pain.

"Dinah, go tell everyone and send someone to get the doctor while I take her to the birthing room," said Lydia. Dinah ran while Lydia took Veronica's arm and walked her up the stairs.

Dinah burst through the door, breathing heavily. "Her water has broken, and we need the doctor."

Nobody moved for a second, then everyone jumped up.

"Adrian, would you mind getting Doctor Angers?" asked Henry.

"Right away," he said as he exited the room.

Ellen and Ann left the room and headed up the stairs excitedly, talking about the baby finally getting here and leaving the men in the dining room.

Owen stood at the head of the table, not knowing what to do. Henry looks at Callum, smiling as he nods his head toward Owen. Callum walks to Owen and pats him on the shoulder. "Come on, son. Let's go have a drink while we wait for the doctor."

"Oh, all right," he replied nervously.

As Henry poured three glasses of port, Callum walked up beside him.

"Do you think we need to snap him out of it?" asked Callum.

Henry turned to see Owen slumped in a chair, staring off as if lost.

"I can snap him out of it," said Henry smiling. Callum chuckled as he sipped his drink.

Henry walked up and sat down in front of Owen, setting a glass in front of him. "Owen, we need to talk about what I am going to do to you. I think it should happen before the baby gets too attached to you," he said with a scowl on his face.

Owen quickly sat up straight, and all the color drained from his face. Callum and Henry could hold back the laughter.

"I believe that did it," said Callum as he sat beside Henry.

Owen relaxed as he realized Henry wasn't serious.

"Are you all right, son?"

"I am going to have a baby. I knew I was going to have a baby, but I am having a baby now. I mean, I am not having a baby, Veronica is, but it is coming now," Owen rambled.

"I think I broke him," said Henry, looking at Callum.

"Owen, take a deep breath and calm down. You need to be clear-headed in case you need to make a decision," said Callum.

"Decision? What decision?" Owen asked, getting nervous.

Callum looked at Henry, wondering if they should explain that there could be complications or just let it go. Henry slightly shook his head no.

"When the doctor gets here, you might need to talk to him, and you do not want to sound like a nitwit," said Henry.

"Oh," said Owen as he took a deep breath and calmed down. "You are right. I need to be level-headed."

Upstairs, Veronica was in her gown and trying to walk around. Ellen and Ann were on either side as a contraction hit and caused her to fail. The pains were still far apart and not too intense. Ellen noticed that every time Veronica had a contraction, Dinah seemed uneasy.

"Oh, that one hurt. I need to sit down," said Veronica as she approached the bed. But when they got more intense after a while, she couldn't hold in the groans.

"Dinah, would you go and see if the doctor has arrived? If not, would you wait and show him the way here?" asked Ellen.

"Yes," she said as she walked toward the door.

"Oh, and check on the hot water and towels. They should have it about ready."

"Yes, ma'am."

After Dinah left the room, Ellen looked at Ann, smiling. "I think we need to keep Dinah outside. She was about to faint."

"Yes, she has never had a very strong constitution," Ann said, chuckling.

"Lydia, will you be okay?" asked Ellen.

"Yes, I will be fine."

Ellen walked over to Lydia and wrapped her arms around her shoulder. "You have been a good friend to her. I am so happy for you and Adrian." Veronica let out a loud moan that got everyone's attention.

"They are getting stronger," she said as she tried to climb up on the bed. They helped her to sit with her back against the headboard.

The doctor finally arrived, and after checking Veronica, he let everyone know she was doing fine, and it shouldn't be much longer.

Dinah and a couple of servants arrived with hot water and many towels.

"Dinah, I need you to bring some chairs and place them outside the door. The men will be diligent and wait outside until the baby arrives. You need to keep them from coming in until we tell them they can," said Ellen.

Dinah looked at her, confused.

"I know Henry. If he hears his daughter scream, he will break down the door to make sure she is all right."

"Oh, how will I keep him out?"

"Take Callum off to the side and tell him what I said."

"Okay, I will do my best." She looked at Veronica and thought, *I am never having kids.* She then left to get some servants to help bring chairs.

It wasn't long, and the men were sitting outside the door as Ellen said they would. As time went by, the contractions became unbearable. Once the doctor said it was time, they moved her to the birthing chair. Lydia was to her right, Ellen to her left, and Ann stood at her head.

"Miss Veronica. I need you to push," said Doctor Angers.

She took a deep breath and pushed, letting out a painful yell.

"I hope my little girl will be okay," said Henry.

"Henry, I have never met a more brickly young lady than your daughter. She is a real credit to the weaker gender. I know a few men who should take lessons from her about being strong," said Callum patting Henry's shoulder.

"Veronica is so like her mother. Loving and kind, but so stubborn. When Leah decided to do something, nothing could stop her." Henry got a faraway look in his eyes. Then they heard Veronica scream and jumped to their feet toward the door. Callum and Dinah stood in front of the door to keep Henry and Owen from entering.

"No, Henry, you cannot go in until they come out and say you can. I know you are worried, but she will be all right."

The door opened before Henry could say anything else, and Lydia emerged. "Everything went well. They are getting Veronica in bed and the baby cleaned up.

"They are, all right?" asked Owen. They could hear a baby crying inside the room.

"Yes. The baby is beautiful," she said, smiling. Adrian walked up to her, and she hugged him. "It will not be long, and everyone can come in," she said as she opened the door and walked back in.

It wasn't but a minute, and the door opened, and the doctor walked out. "The baby is healthy, and the mother is doing fine."

Ellen walks up behind him. "Would you like to come in and see the baby?" she asked.

The doctor stepped aside and let the men walk in. They saw Veronica in bed, looking down at the bundle in her arms. She looked up and smiled. Owen walked up to her side, and the rest stood around him, peering down at the baby.

"It is a girl," said Veronica. Everyone started talking happily. "Would you like to hold her?" Veronica asked Owen.

He bent down and took the baby in his arms. "She is beautiful," he said with so much love in his eyes.

"She has a head full of black hair," said Henry.

"Have you decided on a name?" asked Callum.

Everyone looked at Veronica, waiting for an answer. "Yes, we talked about it. We named her after someone who could not be here," said Veronica, looking at her father.

"Leah," said Henry.

"Yes, Leah."

Both Henry and Ellen smiled with tears in their eyes.

"Leah Pierce. That's a beautiful name," said Callum.

"She would love that," said Ellen.

"Leah Lanniah Pierce," said Veronica.

"Lanniah?" asked Lydia.

"Yes. It is Lydia, Hannah, and Dinah. I wanted to name her after all three of my best friends."

Both Lydia and Dinah were happily surprised.

"It is beautiful," said Dinah trying not to cry. Lydia wrapped her arm around Dinah's shoulder.

"Yes, it is. That means so much," said Lydia.

"Come on, everyone. Let us give the new mom and dad some time with little Leah," said Ann.

Owen sat down on the bed, facing Veronica. He leaned over and pulled back a little of the blanket to reveal the baby's face.

"She looks so much like you," said Veronica.

"You think so?"

"Yes, I do."

"Look at all the black hair," said Owen as he lightly rubbed her head.

"Are you happy it is a girl?" asked Veronica.

"Yes, so happy," he said, looking at Veronica with a big smile.

Veronica was thankful she had a girl. That way, when Owen remarried, their baby won't be in danger from a greedy, title-hungry woman.

Not long after Owen left the room, Veronica had just finished feeding little Leah when she heard a knock. Lydia peeked her head in.

"Someone is here to see you," she said as she stepped aside, and Ellis walked in.

"You came."

"Of course, as soon as I got the message you had the baby," he said as he walked up to the bed.

"You want to hold your niece?"

"It is a girl?"

"They did not tell you?"

"I did not stop to talk to anyone. When I arrived, I saw Lydia, and she brought me straight here," he said as he took the baby in his arms.

"What did you name her?"

"Leah."

"After mom. Look at all that hair."

"Yes, I had considered naming her after Ellen and Ann, but our mother will never get to hold her or watch her grow."

"Hello, little Leah," said Ellis as he walked around, holding the baby close.

Veronica smiled as she watched her brother talk to her baby.

"I bet the grandparents are beside themselves with having their first grandchild," said Ellis as he sat in a chair beside the bed.

"Yes, I am pretty sure they are. I can only imagine how spoilt she will be."

"Oh, I intend to be her favorite uncle."

"You are her only uncle," said Veronica chuckling.

"Exactly. I am going to make you rotten. But I promise to protect you from anything and anyone."

Tears formed in her eyes as she watched her brother make promises to protect her. The love was evident on his face.

"Ellis, I need your promise that you will be here for her if something happens to me. I know Father and Mother will, and Owen will be a great father." She stopped talking as she thought of what to say.

"You are worried about her being mistreated by people. Like you were."

"Yes, even though Father protected me from men, he never knew what was happening until I told Mom," she said as a tear rolled down her face.

"I know she is going to be beautiful, but just in case she looks like me, I want to know there will be someone who knows what could be happening. I cannot stand the thought of her going through that."

"I promise you, when she is older, I will have her watched. I will make sure nobody ever hurts her the way they did you. I am sorry I did not notice what was happening. I wish you had told me sooner."

"That is over now," Veronica said, wiping her face and smiling.

"Yes, the main culprit has been dealt with."

"Ada is a different person now. She has learned her lesson the hard way. The ton has turned on her, and so have her friends," said Veronica, looking sad.

"You do not seem pleased."

"I know you think I am foolish, but I do not take pleasure in Ada's downfall. Since her mother is out of her life, she has become better. I do not want the cruelty of society to cause her to go back to being a horrible person."

"After all these years, you still amaze me. There is nobody out there like you. That girl tormented you, and still, you want to help her," said Ellis, shaking his head.

"We are supposed to forgive and help when we can. It is the right thing to do. I hope you will not be cruel to Ada if you come across her. I am not asking you to be her friend, just do not add to her misery."

Ellis sat looking at Veronica, amazed at how someone could be so good, when little Leah started making noise, trying to wake up.

"Her, let me have her," said Veronica, holding her arms.

"No way, she is mine now," said Ellis playfully.

"All right, you can change her napkins," Veronica said, smiling.

Ellis froze and then walked to Veronica. "Here you go back to your mom."

Veronica couldn't help but laugh at how fast Ellis unhanded Leah.

"Well, I am going to go say hi to everyone downstairs," he said as he made his way to the door.

"Ellis?"

"Yes."

"Be nice."

Ellis smiled. "Always," he said as he left.

As Ellis walked into the dayroom, everyone grew quiet. Owen stood and walked towards Ellis, ready for whatever might happen. Nobody moved as Ellis and Owen stood face to face. Ellis bawled up his fist and struck Owen, sending him flying backward. Callum went to get up, but Henry grabbed his arm, stopping him.

Owen stood up and walked back to Ellis. "Go ahead. I deserve it."

Ellis stood, looking at Owen with so much anger. "You were my friend," he said as he relaxed, "and now you are the father of my beautiful niece." A smile grew on his face. He held out his hand, and Owen stared at it, confused.

He then grabbed it with a massive smile on his face. "I have a little girl."

"I know," said Ellis laughing. Then, everybody relaxed, and the celebration continued.

While everybody was talking, James walked in. "Lord Corbyn and family are here."

"Show them in," said Henry. "Archie, good to see you," said Henry as he held out his hand.

When Ellis saw Hannah, he tensed. She didn't look his way even though she saw him standing with Owen by the window.

"Congratulations on the new arrival. As soon as we heard about the baby, Hannah begged us to come to see."

Ellen walked up to Eleanor, hugging her. "Would you two like to see our girl?"

"She had a girl?" asked Hannah.

"Yes, come this way," said Ellen as they left the room.

Veronica lay in bed, and the baby was sleeping beside her as they entered the room. "Hannah, so glad to see you," she said, scooting up to lay her back on the headboard.

She and Eleanor walked to her side, peering down at the baby lying asleep.

"Oh, she is beautiful and looks like Dinah," said Hannah.

"What a head full of black hair," said Eleanor.

"Would you like to hold her?" asked Veronica.

"Oh, yes, I would," said Hannah. She then reached down and picked her up.

Eleanor and Ellen left the room, giving the girls time to talk.

"Veronica, she is so beautiful. I cannot wait to have my own."

"I cannot wait for our kids to play together," said Veronica, smiling.

"Oh, I remember the first time Dinah and I went with you to the castle. We were what, fourteen? That was so much fun, and now when we all have children, they will get to do the same thing."

"Does that mean you have decided to accept an offer?" Veronica never brought Ellis up when they talked about marriage. She hated seeing her friend hurt over her stupid brother.

"I do not know yet, but I need to make up my mind," she said, smiling.

"Well, hurry up. Little Leah needs a playmate."

They sat for a while, talking and making plans once they all had kids.

Down in the dayroom, everyone was in groups, talking.

"Ellis, I might need your help with something."

"What?"

"It is about Lydia and Adrian," said Owen in a low voice.

"Let us go somewhere a little more private," said Ellis.

So, they left the room and went to the office, where Owen explained that Adrian was taking over an estate and the problem they might have with talking to his brother.

"I do not know how to get Adrian's brother here. I have never met the man."

"I have. Before I found out what he tried to do to Adrian, we had investments together. As soon as I knew, I started distancing myself from him. I will come across him from time to time, and he always wants to work together. So far, I have avoided the situation, but I could get him here under the pretense of wanting to invest."

"Yes, that sounds perfect."

Owen left for business the next day, leaving the grandparents at home to help Veronica.

They were in the sitting room playing cards when James came in. "Lord Claridge and his daughter are here, my lord."

"Show them in," said Henry. Everyone stood as they entered.

Ada stood behind her dad with her head down.

"We wanted to come by to say congratulations on the new arrival."

"We are so happy to have her. She is so beautiful," said Callum.

Ellen saw Ada and walked to her. "Ada, would you like to see the baby?"

Ada raised her head and looked surprised. She then looked at her dad, as if asking for permission. He nodded, saying yes.

"Do you think Veronica would mind?"

"Not at all. Come with me," said Ellen as she wrapped her arm around her shoulder, leading her out of the room.

"How is she doing?" asked Henry.

"It has been hard on her, but I am very pleased with how she is handling it."

"Glad to hear. If you need any help, you can count on me," said Callum.

"Thank you, thank all of you, for everything."

Upstairs, Ellen knocks on the door.

"Come in."

"You have a visitor," said Ellen as she walked in. Ada hung back, wondering if she should be there.

"It is okay. Come on in," said Ellen seeing Ada hesitating.

Veronica was sitting in bed, wondering who was outside. Then, finally, Ada walked in but kept her head down. "Ada, glad you came."

Ada looked up and saw Veronica smiling at her, and she relaxed.

"Would you like to see the baby? She is here," said Veronica, pointing to the small crib that was beside her.

Ada walked over and peered down at the little girl, sound asleep. "She is beautiful."

Ellen left the room, shutting the door and giving them privacy.

"You can hold her," said Veronica.

Ada slowly bent down and took little Leah in her arms. She sat in the chair beside the crib and stared at the sleeping baby. "She looks like Dinah."

"That is what Hannah said," Veronica said, laughing.

"How are you?" asked Ada.

"I am good. Sore but good. How have you been?"

"All right," said Ada as she softly touched the baby's head.

"Really?"

Ada looked up. "It's been hard, but people leave me alone now."

"Good."

Ada stood and slowly put Leah back in her crib. "I need to get back. Father is probably ready to leave."

"I am glad you came to see the baby."

"She is beautiful." Ada then turned to walk to the door but stopped when she grabbed the doorknob. She turned her head back to look at Veronica. "I do not know how you can be so nice to me after everything I did. It means a lot to me."

"You are going to be okay. Good things are coming your way."

"Thank you," said Ada, leaving the room.

Two weeks later, the day finally arrived to confront Adrian's brother. Ellis entered the office where Veronica and Owen were waiting.

"David should be here any time," said Ellis as he sat beside Veronica.

"Where is Adrian?"

"We decided to wait until we have him at least sitting before we bring Adrian in," said Owen.

"That is a good idea. We do not want him running out of here before we have a chance to talk."

At that time, James walked in. "Lord David Cartwright is here."

"Send him in," said Ellis as he stood to greet him.

As David walked in, he saw Ellis approaching him. Owen stood by the desk, and Veronica sat on the couch. But, of course, he wasn't expecting anyone but Ellis.

"Lord Cartwright," said Ellis.

"Hello, Lord Aldridge. I was glad to hear from you."

"This is my brother-in-law, Lord Pierce."

"Good to meet you, Lord Pierce."

"And this is my sister, Lady Veronica."

David walked over and held out his hand as she stood. As he leaned down to kiss her hand, she noticed his eyes raking over her body. Feeling revolted, she quickly removed her hand but recovered with a smile.

"Lord Cartwright, welcome to my home," she said calmly.

"Please, call me David."

"That would not be appropriate, Lord Cartwright," Veronica says as the smile left her face.

"David, please sit," says Ellis, sitting in a chair beside the coach. Owen also sat next to Veronica. He did not get a good feeling from David and wondered how everything would work. "The reason we have asked you here is to discuss a situation that involves you and your brother," said Ellis.

"My brother? He disappeared almost a year ago and is presumed dead." They all could see his body stiffen at the mention of his brother.

"Oh, he is not dead," said Veronica.

"How do you know this?"

"Let us get this out in the open. Adrian has acquired an estate and wants to rejoin society before he gets married," said Ellis.

"Pardon me for a minute," said Owen as he stood and left the room.

"I do not know what any of you are getting at. I have nothing to do with my brother. So, if you will excuse me, I will take my leave." David stood, but before he could take a step, the door opened, and Adrian walked in.

"Hello, David. I guess it is a disappointment to see me alive."

David stood there, not knowing what to say, as he stared at his brother. Then, quickly recovering, he stepped forward and extended his hand in an attempt to seem pleased.

"It is good to see you, Adrian. I thought you had met an untimely death."

"Yes, I am sure you did. I need you to sit back down and listen to what I have to say," said Adrian as he sat next to Ellis.

David returned to his seat, eyeing his brother.

"As they have probably already informed you. I have acquired an estate and will shortly be getting married. Therefore, I will not interfere with your life in any form or fashion. I want to be left alone to live my life in peace."

David sat in silence as he thought about Adrian being alive and sitting right before him.

"You do not want to claim your rightful place?"

"No."

"How will you explain where you have been?"

"I was traveling abroad and was unaware people thought I was dead. You did not know. Since we have never been close, it will not be hard to believe."

"And that is it? We will leave each other alone?" asked David, not believing it could be that simple.

"Yes, David. I do not want any trouble."

"Okay. If that is truly what you intend, then I will not be any hindrance to you."

"May I say something?" asked Veronica. Everyone remained silent as they looked at Veronica. "Adrian is marrying a good friend of mine. So, if anything should happen to them, whoever is responsible will pay dearly," she said calmly.

David stared at her for a few seconds, then smiled. "When you first came out, I made some inquiries about you. Everyone said you were like your mother. Sweet, timid, easily compliant. They underestimated you. I believe you are more like your father."

"You have no idea," said Ellis, smiling.

"Fine, Adrian. I will not interfere with your life. Now, if you excuse me, I will be on my way," he said as he stood up.

Before David left the room, he stopped, turned back, and looked at Adrian. No emotion was visible on his face, but Veronica had been watching him since he entered the room, and he had so much hatred in his eyes for his brother. She hoped that enough people aware of the situation would keep him from doing something stupid.

"Well, now, that went well," Veronica said, smiling.

Ellis chuckled. "I am going to go. I do have business to attend to," hes said as he hugged his sister.

Adrian walked up to Ellis and held out his hand. "Thank you, Lord Aldridge."

" Just Ellis, Adrian. If you need any help, do not hesitate to ask."

"I will, thank you."

After Ellis left, everyone sat down and relaxed. Lydia walked in, looking very nervous.

"It is okay, sweetheart. I think we are going to be safe," said Adrian. She walked over and sat down beside him, and he wrapped his arms around her, pulling her close.

"Now, we need to start introducing you two back into society. There is a ball in a month. That should give us enough time to get ready, and I should be able to attend, so we need to take you shopping. You also, Adrian, but I will leave you in Owen's capable hands," said Veronica as she stood and left the room.

"Well, Adrian, I guess we had better get started," said Owen.

Lydia laughed "Yes, you do not want to be unprepared when Veronica is on a mission."

"No, I do not," said Owen as he hurriedly got up but stopped at the door and looked back. "Well, come on, Adrian."

Adrian looked at Lydia and laughed as he got up and followed Owen.

A month went by fast, and they were on their way to the ball. Veronica had already requested two extra invites for Lady Lydia McBride, the late Lord Vernon McBride's daughter, and Lord Adrian Cartwright, who had just returned from abroad. Rumors were running rampant about the two, which was expected.

In the carriage, Lydia was about to pass out. Adrian held her hand and tried to reassure her that everything would be okay.

"You look beautiful," said Veronica. Lydia wore a lavender gown with silver embroidery on the bodice and hem. It was beautiful and fit her perfectly, complimenting her pale skin and golden hair.

The carriage came to a stop. Lydia took a deep breath and exited. As they entered the ballroom, everyone came to a halt and stared at them. Veronica smiled and leaned in to whisper in her ear.

"It is Adrian they are staring at. You need to be sure and reveal that you two are engaged."

"I think I am going to be sick," said Lydia as her face grew pale.

"Breathe," said Veronica as several men and women approached them. Most were old friends of Adrian's. A few girls had been friends with Ada when Lydia was part of their group. Lydia was polite but not overly friendly, as she noticed none spoke to Veronica.

"Why do you not come over here with us?" said one of the girls.

"No, thank you. I wish to stay with my friend and betroth."

"Betroth?"

"Yes, I am engaged to Lord Adrian Cartwright."

"Does he have any wealth? I was informed his brother would retain the title and fortune," said another girl, looking down her nose at Lydia.

"You have not heard? Lord Cartwright had just acquired an estate in New Castleton. They will be moving there after the wedding," said Veronica. Her eyes dared the girl to say anything else.

"That is fantastic," said another girl trying to lighten the conversation.

The rest of the evening went smoothly. Everyone seemed to accept Adrian's story, and Lydia went to France after her mother died to live with relatives. That was where she met Adrian and fell in love. After Lydia calmed down, she enjoyed the night.

Veronica was happy that everything went perfectly. One less thing she had to do before she could leave. Now, the hard part: talking to her father.

# CHAPTER
# TWENTY-SIX

There are far, far better things ahead
than any we leave behind.

C.S. Lewis

Stepping into her father's house did not make her happy, knowing how upset she was about to make him, but she needed to get things over with to move to Scotland before winter set in.

"Hello, Ronnie. How are you, and where is the baby?" asked Ellen as she hugged her.

"She is at home. I thought about bringing her, but I need to talk to Father about some personal things."

"You still want a divorce?"

"How did you know?"

"Meredith," said Ellen smiling.

"That makes sense. You did not tell Father?"

"No, I was waiting to see if you changed your mind. Sometimes, feelings can grow between people, especially after a baby comes along."

"I wish that had been the case. I also wish things had not happened, but they did," she said, looking away, trying to hide her pain.

Ellen saw it anyway. Before she could reply, Henry came into the room.

"Where is my granddaughter?"

"Hello, Father. Good to see you too."

Henry walked up to her and kissed her on the forehead. "I am happy to see you. Now, where is my little Leah?"

"She is at home. I needed to speak to you about some things."

"Okay, this sounds serious. Let us go to my office," said Henry as he walked Veronica out of the room and into his office. He sat behind the desk, and Veronica sat on the chair facing him. "Now, tell me what is going on."

Veronica took a deep breath and let it out. "I need your help in getting a divorce."

He sat back and stared at her for a few seconds before speaking. "I am guessing you cannot get over all that has happened?"

"I want to get away from everything. London, society, all of it. I know I will never be able to remove myself altogether because one day Leah will have her come out, but that is not for several years."

"And Owen is okay with this?"

Veronica looked down as she thought about Owen.

"He does not want a divorce, does he?"

"I do not know if he does or does not. We agreed after I found out about the plan Agnes derived. So, it does not matter what he wants." She didn't want to sound heartless, but it was the truth.

"I watched him when you had your baby. I believe he has fallen in love with you, and I know there was a time you were in love with him."

"Yes, you are right. I was in love with him, but things changed." Veronica was hoping her father would not ask what it was because she could not talk about it. Just thinking about it brought tears to her eyes, and the pain in her heart grew stronger.

"Are you sure about this? I do not want you to wake up one day and regret this decision."

"I have had a year to think about it. I need this. And..." She stopped talking, not sure about telling him she was leaving for Scotland.

"What are you not telling me?"

"Once the divorce is finished, I will be moving to Scotland." She closed her eyes, preparing herself for the yelling that was coming.

"You are going to take my grandbaby and move to that castle?" he said as he stood angrily.

Ellen had been eavesdropping outside and decided she needed to interfere.

"Father, it will not be so bad. I will come to visit, and you and Mother can come up there," she stayed seated, trying to defuse her father's temper.

"No, you are not taking her up there so she can become a wild hellion," he said as if the discussion was over.

"Now, honey, calm down," said Ellen as she sat beside Veronica.

"Father, I spent half my life up there," said Veronica.

"That is not helping," said Ellen in a low voice.

"My point exactly," said Henry as he sat back down as if he had won the argument.

"I was not that bad," said Veronica in a low voice. "I will come to visit often. And when she gets older, she can come and stay. She will be here quite a lot with Owen and his family. I plan to have a big Christmas this year, as it will be her first. But, father, I need to leave. I need to get away."

Veronica was quiet as she watched her father look down, and the anger left his face. When he looked back up, she saw tears in his eyes.

She got up and went to him, wrapping her arms around him as he sat in his chair.

"I will miss you," he said, hugging her back.

"I promise we will get together every chance. I want you and Mother to be a big part of Leah's life."

Veronica straightened up, and Henry stood facing her.

"Yes, her grandpa will be a big part of her life. I will go to parliament and get you that divorce, but I need you to go home and get a room ready for your mother and me. I intend on staying with you for a couple of days to be close to my grandbaby."

Veronica looeds at Ellen, surprised.

"Oh, yes, I would love to see my grandbaby," said Ellen.

"Okay." Veronica then kissed her dad's cheek and hugged her mother. As she walked to the door, she said, "I will go home and get your room ready." She never turned around.

"She is hurt because of me," said Henry.

"What are you talking about?" asked Ellen as she approached him.

He stoof and wrapped his arms around her. "She married him because of me. I should not have asked her to give him a chance," he said as he buried his head in her shoulder.

"Oh, my love, you cannot blame yourself for what happened. If someone is at fault, it is me for making Agnes an enemy. I made our family a target."

"Are we not a pair? Blaming ourselves for what someone else has done," said Henry.

They stood hugging each other for some time, relying on each other to find comfort from their guilt.

A week later, Henry held Leah while Ellen and Veronica sat on the couch talking.

"Veronica," said Henry, interrupting their conversation on the latest fashion.

"Yes, father?"

"You still need to show Owen the divorce papers. Have you?"

"No, not yet. I wanted to wait until I had everything in order and you two had finished your visit with Leah. I am also taking her to Owen's parents for a day before I leave."

"That is good of you to make sure they have a little time with her before you leave," said Ellen.

"We have talked and decided to come to Scotland a month before Christmas and stay till spring. If that is all right with you?" asked Henry.

Veronica's face lit up at the thought of her family being there for so long. "Yes, that is great. Thank you so much for everything," she said, looking at her mom and dad.

The next day, after her parents left, she took little Leah to the Pierce home for a visit. While Ann and Dinah were preoccupied with the baby, Veronica asked Callum if they could speak privately.

Once they entered the study, Veronica and Callum sat by the fire.

"I wanted to bring Leah over for a visit because I have decided to leave soon for Scotland."

"You are going to leave Owen," he said more as a statement than a question.

"Yes."

"I knew you were not happy. I could see it in your eyes when you thought no one was watching you. My son has ruined what could have been the best thing in his life."

"He did what he thought was best for his family and the woman he loved at the time. It was a valuable lesson for the both of us," said Veronica.

"I hope what has happened has not hurt you to the point that you cannot find happiness."

"I have Leah. She is all the happiness I need," Veronica could not help but smile as she thought of her baby girl.

"Yes, she is the best thing that came out of this."

"My family is coming to Scotland in November and staying until spring. Your family is invited as well. I want Owen and all of you to have as much time as you wish with Leah. I want her to have a large family full of love."

"Then we shall come as well. I know Dinah would like to see what a Christmas would be like at a castle," Callum said, chuckling.

"Then I will be expecting you," she said as she stood. Before she reached the door, she stopped and turned around.

"Would you please keep watch over Owen? I would feel at ease if I knew you would see to him."

"Of course, I will. I also hope you can find peace."

"Thank you," she said as they left the room to join the rest of the family.

That evening she returned home, calling all the staff into the library.

"I have called all of you here to inform you I will be moving to my home in Scotland soon. Owen will remain here as the owner of this house. I do not want any of you to worry. Your positions are secure, and Owen will be an excellent lord."

"Can any of us go with you, my lady?" asked Ian.

"If any would prefer to move, I will welcome you wholeheartedly. Do you wish to come, Ian?"

"Scotland is my home."

"Our home," said Michael.

"Truly?" asked Veronica, surprised.

Ian smiled. "We learned to sound English, but our heart is in Scotland," he said with a Scottish brogue.

"How come I never knew this? And yes, you and any others are welcome to come or stay. It is entirely your decision. However, I do hope those who stay will show Lord Pierce the same loyalty everyone has shown me," she said happily, knowing at least Ian and Michael had left the room.

"May we ask why?" asked Ian.

"Owen and I are divorcing, and I want to go to my home."

"I see. Well, we will be going with you and would also hope to remain in service to you. Whatever place you might have."

"I am so happy the both of you will be joining me."

They both nodded and left the room, leaving Veronica in the library. Now came the hard part: talking to Owen.

When Owen returned home, he found Veronica watching the fire in the library on the couch.

"How was your visit with Mother and Father?" he asked as he walked around the couch. Then, seeing Leah lying beside Veronica, he sat down and softly rubbed her head.

"It was good." She could see the love he had for his little girl, which caused pain of regret in her heart for what she was about to do. She got up and opened the door, calling for the nanny.

"Abby, will you take Leah to her bed, please?"

Owen looked at Veronica and knew she wanted to talk. Owen stood and faced her. "What do you want to talk about?"

"Over here," she said as she walked to the desk.

He followed and noticed a document sitting on the desk. He didn't even have to read it to know what it was. He looked at Veronica, but she couldn't look at him. She was afraid she would see the pain in his eyes. "I was hoping you would change your mind. I do not want a divorce. I want to try to be a family."

"I know. I am sorry, but I cannot stay. I need to get away from everything."

"You cannot forgive me?" he said, walking over to the window and looking out into the dark.

"It is not about that. You marrying me for the money was not a surprise, and wanting to divorce me, well, I can understand that."

He turned around and walked up to her. "Then what is it?"

When she looked up at him, he saw tears running down her face. There was so much pain in her eyes. "You slept with someone else on our wedding night. It haunts me. I feel so much pain inside. Sometimes, I cannot breathe." Tears fall freely down her face as she stoppeds trying to hide her feelings.

Owen closed his eyes and lowered his head. "I am so sorry, and I wish I could go back and change what I did. I never intended for that to happen."

"I know you never wanted to hurt me like that, but it happened, and I need to go away to try and stop the pain. I feel broken."

Owen leaned his head down, and they touch their foreheads together. "I do not want to let you go. I love you," Owen said as a tear left his closed eyes.

"I am sorry. I just cannot stay," she said as she backed away. "Please, sign them," she said as she turned to leave.

"Please, do not go," he said, causing Veronica to stop.

The memory of that night replayed in her head.

"Lydia is getting married in two days. I am leaving the day after." She then walked out, leaving Owen staring at the door.

Lydia looked beautiful in her wedding gown as she walked down the aisle toward the man she loved. Veronica had a smile on her face even though she felt nauseated. Being there brought back the memory of her wedding. How happy she had been. How much she had loved Owen. If only she had known that her marriage would end on her wedding night. She concentrated on her breathing to keep her tears back. She had to make sure Lydia's day was perfect.

Owen sat beside her with his head down most of the time. She could tell he was having a hard time sitting there, acting like everything was fine. Finally, Veronica reached over and held his hand, letting him know she did understand what he was feeling.

The wedding breakfast went smoothly, and when the guest finally left, Veronica and Lydia went into the sitting room to talk privately.

"Thank you so much for everything," said Lydia as she hugged Veronica.

"Bringing you to my home was one of the most fortunate things I could have done. I am so glad you found someone that makes you happy. Now, do not forget you are coming out for Christmas. You might have so much to do at your new home, but you can take the time to relax."

"Oh, yes, I plan on it."

"You need to get going. Adrian is eagerly waiting for you."

Lydia hugged her and left the room. Veronica was finally able to stop smiling. It was strange how putting on a fake happy expression could be painful after a while.

She walked over to the couch, plopped down, laying her head back and closing her eyes. Owen walked in and stared, taking in everything about her and engraving it in his memory. He then turned and left, going to his office, knowing that if he stayed, he would beg her not to leave him.

Veronica walked down the stairs and noticed the last of her trunks were being taken out to the coach. The rest of her things would be sent later. Veronica walked over to Abby, who was waiting outside the sitting room. She decided to go with Veronica and remain as Leah's nanny. Veronica was happy because Abby was very good with Leah.

"I guess it is time," said Veronica as she opened the door, and they both walked in. Owen was sitting in a chair facing the fireplace with Leah in his arms.

"Owen, I am sorry, but I need to get going," she said as she motioned for Abby to take Leah from him.

She walked over beside Owen and waited for him to give a sign that he was going to hand her over. Veronica watched as he bent down, kissed Leah's forehead, whispered, "I love you," and then handed her over to Abby. She then left the room to give them some time to talk.

"Owen, I need you to be careful. Now, you are a target for title-hungry mothers and daughters. You already know what a woman can do to get what she wants. So, the best thing to do is ask the servants to inquire about whomever you are interested in courting. Meredith taught me that they are the best about information. I am saying this because you have a daughter to consider, and I do not want anyone like Agnes around her."

She waited for a response but only got a nod. *Is he not going to say anything to me? Not even a goodbye?* Veronica thought as she grew a little irritated.

She walked toward him but stopped when she saw his face. Tears were streaming down his cheeks, eyes puffy from what was obvious he had been crying for a while.

"Owen, I..." Veronica did not know what to say. She did not think he would be this distraught.

"Is this how I made you feel?" asked Owen as he looked at Veronica.

She looked away, not able to meet his eyes. "Is it hard to breathe, to think? You feel like your heart is torn to shreds," said Veronica as tears fell. She doesn't know if it is because of her pain or seeing Owen's, but she cannot stop crying.

"I am so sorry. I understand why you could never forgive me for what I did." He stood and opened his arm, and she walked into them, needing to feel his embrace one last time. So they stood in each other's arms until Veronica stepped back and looked up at him.

He raised his hand to cup her face and wiped her tears with his thumb, and she did the same. "I hope you can somehow let go of the pain and be happy," he said as tears still fell from his eyes.

"I hope you can too." She removed her hand from his face and turned to leave but stopped when she got to the door.

"Your family will be coming for Christmas and staying for a while. I expect you to be with them."

"I will," he said, giving her a slight smile.

She stared at him for a second, then turned and left. Owen sat back down and sobbed as his life walked out the door.

A week later, Ellis walked up and knocked on the door. Elliot opens and, seeing Ellis, stepped back to let him in.

"You got my letter," said Elliot.

"Yes. How is he?"

"Not good. Lord Pierce has not eaten since she left, and he mainly stayed in the cup," said Elliot as he took Ellis's gloves and overcoat.

"Where is he?"

"In the library."

Ellis walked to the library, where he didn't knock but walked on in, finding Owen sitting by the fire with a glass of brandy in his hand. Ellis didn't say anything. He just walked over and sat down across from him. As he took in Owen's appearance, he knew Owen was in bad shape.

His hair was a mess, he had not shaved in days, and his clothes were wrinkled and dirty.

"This was her favorite room. For a few days, I could still smell her perfume," Owen said as he took a sip.

"I know this is hard, but you must get on with your life. You still have a beautiful little girl that needs a father. And I hate to have to kick your arse if you disappoint her," said Ellis, trying to sound stern.

Owen looked up at him, and tears formed in his eyes.

"Owen, I know you are hurting, but what you are doing is making it worse."

"It hurts so much," said Owen, wiping his face with the back of his hand.

"Come on, get up, and let us get you a bath and put on some clean clothes," said Ellis as he grabbed Owen's arm and helped him to stand. His legs were shaky from sitting for so long.

As they left the room, Owen looked at Ellis. "Thank you for still being my friend after everything I did."

"I think you have received enough punishment for your mistake," Ellis said as they left the room.

# CHAPTER
# TWENTY-SEVEN

From the moment I saw her.
I knew this one was worth the broken heart.

Atticus

I t had been two weeks, and Veronica has finally settled in. It took longer than she thought to hire enough staff for so many wanted to come to work for her. She even had a few men she believed only wanted to get close to her. The knowledge of her divorce had already spread, and she was getting visitors she would not see.

Finally having some time, she invited Seinaid over for a weekend, and of course, Liam could not be away from her for so long, came with her. While Liam was doing things with Ian and Michael, Veronica and Seinaid were in the solar room, her private chambers, for Veronica to get away and have some privacy. They talked about many things that had happened, but Veronica had not said anything about why she was divorced.

"Okay, you have been avoiding telling me what happened between you and Owen," said Seinaid as she went to grab her son, who was trying to crawl away. She put him back on the blanket, where little Leah quietly looked around.

"Quite a bit happened, and I do not want anyone to know everything. I had rather they make their own assumptions."

"Okay."

They talked for an hour about what happened, except for Owen sleeping with Ada on her wedding night. That was too painful and humiliating. Veronica could never get the feeling of not being enough for a man out of her head. Seinaid was utterly stunned and didn't know what to say. She had never known someone like that Agnes woman. To want to hurt Veronica like that made Seinaid mad.

"I would love to tie her up and beat her until she begs to die." Veronica looked at Seinaid and started laughing. "I am serious," she said, wondering why Veronica was laughing.

It didn't take a second, and Seinaid started laughing along with her when the door opened, and Sean and Kieran entered. They watched the two women laugh until Veronica saw them. She got up, walked over, and hugged Kieran.

"Good to see you," said Keirin as he hugged her back. She then walked to Sean, and he wrapped his arms around her and hugged her tight.

"Glad you are back, now where is that bairn of yours?" said Sean once he had let go of her.

"She is over here," she said as she walked over to the blanket and picked her up. "Her name is Leah." She handed her to Sean, who couldn't take his eyes off the little girl in his arms.

"She is beautiful, and she has your eyes," he said, looking up at Veronica.

"Yes, I was glad that was what she took from me."

Kieran stood beside Sean, looking at Leah. "We are going to have to watch her close. This one is going to have them chasing after her," said Kieran.

Veronica smiled as she listened to them, planning how they would string up anybody that made their little Leah cry.

"The fall harvest is in two days. You should go and let everyone see you are doing fine. Everyone in town is talking about you returning and no longer being married," said Seinaid.

"She is right," said Kieran as he picked up Acair and started playing with him.

"Are all of you going?"

"Aye, me and Liam will be going for a short time. I am afraid he is still nervous about losing us. He has gotten better but not enough to leave Acair for very long."

"What about you, Sean?" asked Veronica.

"Aye, I will be going."

"Okay, I will go," she said, walking over to look at Leah, who had fallen asleep in Sean's arms. "You are good with her," she said, smiling at him.

Sean couldn't help but stare at Veronica. He didn't know what had happened between her and Owen, but he could see sadness in her eyes.

At that time, Railbert walked in, letting them know supper was ready. Veronica was so happy to see him again. He had changed so much being back home. She would have trouble telling them apart if his hair weren't greyer than his brother's since Railbert smiles now.

"It is still a surprise to me Ailbert has a twin brother," said Sean after Abby left with Leah and Railbert took Acair to the nursery.

"That is because Railbert went with my mother to England when she married. He stayed until I married. I am glad he wanted to continue to work here," she said as they sat down for dinner.

The festival was exciting for Veronica. It had been years since she had attended. After meeting with everyone, they walked around enjoying the food, watching the games, and even participating in some. Veronica signed up for the archery competition, to everyone's surprise. Nobody knew she was an expert bowman and could yield a sword with the best of them. Her grandfather taught her, but it was kept quiet, for he feared Henry would stop letting Veronica stay with him.

When the competition started, the men joked about a woman thinking she could compete with the men. Veronica just smiled and walked up to the first line. She took a deep breath and let it fly right in the center. Everyone was shocked at first but started talking about beginner's luck, making Sean mad.

He went to walk over when Veronica grabbed his arm. "Let them talk," she said, smiling at him.

"They need to learn some respect," he said, glaring at the men.

"Sometimes people make poor judgments when their pride is hurt. Just wait until this is over. You can say something if I win, and they still wish to insult me."

Kieran walked up and stood by Sean. "And I will help," he said, giving Sean a smile that Veronica knew meant there would be more than just words.

She smiled, happy they were still her friends after being gone for so long.

Veronica's aim never faltered the further she moved from the target. The men that once heckled her were quiet as more competitors were eliminated.

It was finally down to the last two. Veronica was one of them, drawing a large crowd. The man standing next to her made his shot and barely missed the center of the target. Everyone clapped and hollered for the man, and some even patted him on the shoulder. But Veronica could have heard a pin drop when she stepped up and prepared for her turn.

She took a deep breath and let it out slowly as she aimed. Then, letting her arrow fly, she stayed frozen as it landed. It seemed like the whole crowd had held their breath along with Veronica until the man standing down the field went to see where her arrow landed.

"DEAD CENTER," was heard, and the crowd went crazy.

Sean picked up Veronica and spun her around as she laughed. Then, after several hugs from everyone, including Liam, the beaten man walked up. Nobody said a word as they observed him.

"I have never seen a lass that could shoot like that."

"Do you think Tyrin Brannon would not make sure his granddaughter was a warrior?" she said, smiling at the man.

"Aye, that he would and did," he said, bowed, and walked off.

"We need to have a drink and celebrate," said Kieran.

"Yes, I could stand to sit for a spell," said Veronica.

"Seinaid, Liam are you coming?" asked Kieran.

Seinaid looked up at Liam with big, pleading eyes. Liam laughed, knowing he can't say no to her.

"For a little while," he said. Sienaid smileed big and hugged him.

They entered the tavern filled with people having a good time. After finding a table near the back, Sean and Keirin went to get some drinks.

"I am impressed with your bow skills," said Liam.

"You should see her with a sword," said Seinaid.

Liam looked at Veronica with a questionable look.

"It seems all the men in my life wanted me to know how to defend myself. No one, except Ellis knows our grandfather taught me to fight."

Once Sean and Kieran got back, everyone was talking and laughing. Several people came up and congratulated Veronica and spoke about her skills.

"Why is everyone acting as if she belongs here?" a voice rose above the crowd. Everyone grew quiet as they looked at a man standing by a table. He was one of the participants in the archery contest that Veronica defeated.

Sean and Kieran stood to go after the man but were stopped by Veronica.

"Let him speak," she said as she stood and faced the man.

"You come here with your tail between your legs, expecting us to welcome you. Why? Because you live in that castle. You husband did not even want you, why should we? Who do ye think you are?"

Veronica tried to look like those words didn't sting, but everyone looked away, embarrassed by his words.

"I will tell you who she is," said someone, and the crowd moved to show a man around her father's age stepping forward. He seemed familiar to Veronica, but she couldn't remember how she knew him.

"When my son was just a wee ladd, he went too far in the woods and got lost. He thought if he climbed a tree, he could see his home, but he fell and broke his leg. Those two," he said as he pointed to Sean and Veronica, "found him. The lass stayed with him while the other went for help. Me and old Tyrin couldn't get to them before it got dark, and a storm blew in. It was the next morning before we found them. She had made a shelter out of tree logs and leaves. Keeping my boy dry and warm. She saved his life." The man walked up to Veronica as he spoke.

"Your father might be English, but you have your mother's heart, and most of us remember Leah. Wasn't a kinder, more caring lass than Leah Brannon. You are brave and fierce, and that is the soul of a Scotsman. Welcome home, lass," he said as he raised his glass.

Then everyone in the tavern stood and raised their glasses. "Welcome home," said everyone, and cheers were heard threw out the building.

Tears welled up in her eyes as she looked at everyone.

"I never thanked you for saving my son," he said as everyone settled back down and returned to enjoying themselves.

"You just did," she said, smiling at him. She then noticed a young boy who looked around fifteen walked up beside the man. Her eyes grew big when she recognized the boy as the one she had helped years ago.

"Alban?" she asked.

"Aye, it is me," he said as he hugged her.

"You have grown so much," she said, looking up at him.

"We had best be on our way," said Alban's father.

"It was good seeing you again, and thank you for your words."

"You are welcome." They then left.

Veronica sat back down, noticing they were all staring at her. "What?"

"I can honestly say it is never boring with you," said Liam, causing everyone to laugh.

"I think it is time we go home," said Seinaid as she looked at Liam.

"I agree. It has been a long day," said Veronica as everyone stood.

"Can I get a ride?" Kieran asked Liam as they left the tavern.

"Sure."

"I am going to go with Veronica. Make sure she gets home safe," said Sean.

Veronica looked up at him with a smile. "That is sweet of you."

After everyone said their goodbyes, Liam waited until they were in the carriage before asking something that had been on his mind all day. "How long has Sean had feelings for Veronica?"

Seinaid and Kieran looked at Liam.

"How do you know?" asked Seinaid.

"It is plain as day. When he looks at her, you can see it."

"Most of his life," said Kieran as he looked out the window, feeling bad for his friend. He had been with Sean when it became too much, and he couldn't hide the pain of loving someone he could never have.

On the ride back to the castle, Sean and Veronica talked about everything that had happened, laughing and joking. They became quiet, and Veronica stared out the window.

"What happened?" asked Sean.

Veronica knew what he was asking. Not sure if it was because she was tired or her nerves were on edge from the confrontation in the tavern, but she couldn't stop the tears from falling. Quickly, he jumped over to her side and held her in his arms as she cried. He felt terrible bringing it up but enjoyed having her in his arms.

Once she stopped crying, she relaxed in his warmth with his arms still around her. She knew she was safe and protected, something she had not felt in a long time. As Sean held her, he noticed how small she seemed in his arms. An overwhelming feeling of wanting to protect her overcame, and he tightened his arms.

"I got your shirt wet," she said, not moving her head off his chest.

"It will dry," he said.

She slowly moved her head back to look up at him. She wanted to thank him for being so comforting but was surprised as she looked into his beautiful, big brown eyes.

When she had been young, she had a crush on him but let it go, knowing her father and grandfather would never allow her to be with him. But being so close to him made her heart beat fast. She only wanted to stay in his arms.

She stopped breathing as she saw him looking at her mouth, and his head slowly moved down. When his lips took hers, she thought her brain had exploded. The sensation was incredible, and she wanted to get as close to him as possible.

Sean didn't know what had come over him, but when she looked up at him, he saw her bright blue eyes looking so sad, he just kissed her. And it was as wonderful as he had imagined. Sean had been with other women, but his heart and mind had always been with Veronica. She tasted like strawberries, and he couldn't get enough of her. The need to breathe was the only reason he stopped.

As they backed away from each other, she thought she saw love in his eyes, causing her to move away from him quickly. Her reaction made Sean think he had done something wrong, but the feeling of wanting her back in his arms was strong.

"I am sorry," he said as he looked away.

*He regrets it, as he should. He cannot care about me. It would only end badly,* she thought, straightening her dress. "It is okay," she said, not looking at him.

The carriage stopped, and he jumped out and waited on her. Sean grabbed her around the waist and lifted her as if she weighed nothing. When he removed his hands, she couldn't help but want them back around her.

"I had better go," he said as he turned to walk away. "You are coming back for the hunt next week?"

"The hunt? The one your grandfather used to have?"

"Yes, I heard it has not happened since he died."

"Dougal outlawed anyone going out hunting on your family land."

"What? Why? How were people feeding their families?"

"They had to buy everything they needed from him."

"That is awful. Well, I told the tavern owner to spread the word. Next week, everyone should be here. I need your help. I know you are one of the best hunters around, so will you come?"

He looked at her and could see she was worried. "Yes, I will come," he said, smiling at her. Veronica's face lit up when she heard him.

"Good, see you then," she said as she turned and walked inside the castle.

Sean was smiling as he walked off. Seeing her happy made him happy.

The day people were going to arrive, Veronica woke early to prepare. She didn't know how many would come but wanted to prepare for a large crowd. As she walked toward the front doors, she saw Ellis's walking in.

"Ellis, you came," she said as she ran towards him. He wraped his arms around her in a tight hug, lifting her off the floor.

"Of course I came. I could not miss it when you wrote that you were starting the hunt. You know how much I enjoyed it when Grandfather hosted it."

"I am so glad. I hope we have a big turnout," she said worriedly.

"Do not fret. I do believe I saw a line of people already on their way. Do you have shield hall ready?"

"Yes, it is ready. Did you see that many coming?" She got excited at the thought.

"Yes, now go get the staff prepared. We need to meet them as they come in."

"The staff are ready. The hall is prepared, and I am scared," she said as she started breathing heavily.

Ellis grabbed her hands. "Okay, take a deep breath. You know what to do, and I am here with you."

She took a deep breath and calmed down. "Okay, I am ready."

They both walked out into the courtyard and saw people coming across the bridge. The line was long, as Ellis had said.

Two tables were lined up on both sides as people walked in to get the family's name and tell them what time they would be hunting.

"Why are there a morning and an afternoon hunt?" asked a man as he signed his family's name.

"As the men bring in the game, the women will start working on getting it ready to smoke or be packed in salt. If there are two hunts, we have time to stay caught up. One big hunt, then we would have an arse load at one time," said Veronica.

The woman at the table looked up at Veronica, shocked at her words, while the man chuckled.

"I understand," he said, then took his family to the next station where they would be told where their quarters would be.

When Veronica looked up, she saw Liam and Seinaid riding in. "I did not expect you two would come."

"I had always wanted to join when your grandfather held it, but my father never let me," said Liam.

"Well, I hope you enjoy it."

Ellis walked up beside Veronica when he saw Seinaid. "Hello, Seinaid," he said, smiling.

"Ellis, it has been a long time," she said as Liam walked up beside her.

"Liam, this is my brother, Ellis," said Veronica as she saw Liam looking protective of Seinaid.

"Ellis, this is my husband," said Seinaid, trying not to laugh.

"It is a pleasure to meet you, Lord Donaldson. Veronica has told me so much about you," he said as he held out his hand.

Liam took his hand and relaxed, knowing he was Veronica's brother. "The same, Lord Aldridge, and it is just Liam."

"Then you must call me Ellis. If you are not busy, would you accompany me to the hall to ensure the men get settled in?"

"Yes, of course, glad to help." Liam leaned down and kissed Seinaid's forehead before he walked off.

When Veronica turned and looked up, Sean stood there, looking at her. She was stunned for a second as her thoughts went to the kiss they had shared.

Seinaid watched the pair, knowing something wasn't right. "Hi, Sean," she said, breaking the awkward silence.

"Hi. Is Kieran here?"

"Not yet. He went to help mother and father before coming."

"Ellis and Liam are taking the men to the hall," said Veronica as she snapped to her senses.

"Ellis is here?" asked Sean, surprised.

"Yes. He will be happy to see you," she said, smiling.

"I will go and help them." Sean took a long look at Veronica before he walked off.

"Okay, spill," said Seinaid.

"We will talk later."

"My lady, may I have a word?"

Veronica looked up and saw a woman holding a little boy's hand. "Yes. How can I help you?"

"I wish to apologize for my husband."

"Your husband?"

"Yes. The man from the tavern. His pride gets the better of him sometimes," said the woman looking down and blushing.

Veronica knew whom she was referring to, and when she looked behind her, she saw the man standing right outside the wall with his head down. "Tell him it is already forgotten, and he is welcome to join the hunt," she said smiling at the woman.

"Thank you, my lady." The woman had a big smile on her face. She then walked toward her husband.

Veronica left the area so the family would feel comfortable while getting situated.

There was a total of twenty-five families, which was more than Veronica thought would come. Once they settled the men in shield hall and the women were paired up and given rooms, it was time to make sure the meal for supper would be ready. A very hearty soup was prepared, and Veronica could tell for some it was the most they had eaten in a while. That would change after the hunt, and she would make sure of it. They would keep hunting until enough was stored to survive the winter.

The children were running around overly about being in the castle, and their mothers were trying to frantically coral them. Veronica had already planned for the children. She had the staff gather all of them together in the main hallway.

"Okay, children, listen up," Veronica said loudly. Railbert and his brother stood behind her and their mothers off to the side. "We are going to take you to a room where there are many toys. I need you all to get in line and follow these two gentlemen. Now do not get out of line because you might get lost and could run into a ghost." Veronica talked in an animated voice, getting the attention of the children.

All the children froze when she said the ghost, and their eyes got big.

"What if the ghosts get in the room?" asked one of the little girls.

"I told the ghost they could not enter the room. You see, the castle is mine, and it has to do what I say," she said with a smile, and all the children seemed to believe her.

Railbert stepped forward and smiled at the children. "All right, let us get in line and remember to stay with us," he said as he walked to the front and started getting the children in line. They then started walking down the hall with Ailbert at the end. One would never have thought two big men like them would be so good with children.

Once the children were gone, Veronica walked over to the mothers. "I hope it was okay with what I told them?"

One of the mothers laughed. "I have not seen my son that still in a long time," she said.

"I cannot believe I will not be chasing my bairns all over the place," said another woman. They all nodded their heads in agreement, happy to have some time to relax.

Veronica turned around and walked back to the hall but stopped upon seeing Sean standing there, smiling. "What are you smiling about?" she asked as she approached him.

"You are great with the little bairns. You should have a castle full of them."

Veronica looked off with a sad expression. "I would have liked that," she said, then walked away.

Sean watched her and wished he could give it to her.

She stopped and turned back, looking at him. "You coming? I need to check on Ellis and see if they need anything."

"Yes, let us go."

They walked beside each other, not saying a word. They could hear the men talking long before reaching the hall, but everyone slowly grew quiet once they entered. Ellis and Liam were speaking to Kieran, Ian, and Michael in the middle of the room. Once they noticed the room had grown quiet, they looked around the hall to see Veronica standing in the doorway. They all walked towards her.

"I was wondering if you needed anything?" she asked as they walked up.

"I think we are good, even though there are more than you planned for," said Ellis smiling.

"Yes, I am well pleased with the turnout. What time are you planning to start the first hunt?"

"We will leave here at dawn."

"Okay, I will have some meat and cheese brought here in the morning for the men to take with them, and the rest can come and eat breakfast in the big dining hall," she said as she watched a young man walking toward them. They all turned to see what she was looking at.

When the man finally stopped, he looked at Ellis. "May I say something to the lady?"

"Yes, of course you can."

He shyly looked at Veronica, then diverted his eyes. "We wanted to thank you for having the hunt. It has been hard ever since Lord Brannon died. This means everything to our families," he said, keeping his eyes down.

"I am sorry I was not here to keep the hunt going. But be sure to let everyone know it will continue every year. So, your families will not have to worry anymore about food for the winter."

"Thank you, my lady," he said as he bowed and left smiling.

"I do believe you just won the hearts of the people," said Ellis.

"I want to make sure no family goes hungry. It is my responsibility now that I am the mistress of Blackthorn."

"If anyone can handle this, it is you," said Ellis, and all the men agreed.

"Thank you, everyone, for having faith in me. I will do my best. Now, I need to ensure the food will be ready for them to take in the morning. If you need anything, let me know."

"Will do, baby sister," said Ellis as he kissed her forehead.

She then left and headed for the kitchen before going to bed. is the next day was going to be exciting and hectic. She prayed everything would go smoothly.

Veronica rose early, before the sun, to ensure everything was ready for the men who had the first hunt. Walking towards the front doors, she saw Ellis talking to the men.

"You are up early," said Kieran as she walked towards them.

"I wanted to ensure everything was ready for the men this morning."

"Yes, sweet sister, everything is good," said Ellis.

The men stopped talking as they heard Veronica talking to Ellis. She noticed them staring at her, so she walked forward to say a few words.

"I am so glad so many of you have come to ensure the families here have plenty to eat this winter. I know you are very skilled, but I want everyone to be careful and return to your family's safe."

All the men thanked her and headed out the front doors.

"Me, Kieran, and Michael are going this morning. Sean, Liam, and Ian will take the group this afternoon. So do not worry, everything will go smoothly," said Ellis as he hugged her and left.

She said a quick prayer to keep them safe.

When she entered the dining hall, she saw Ian and Sean sitting with the rest of the men and women eating breakfast. The entire room grew quiet when they notice her walking in. She smiled at them as she walked toward Sean and sat beside him. He smiled at her but continued to eat.

"What will everyone do until noon?" she asked.

"Double check our weapons, pack our bags, and assign areas to hunt for everyone. Once the first group returns, we will ask where they saw most of the game. That kind of stuff," said Ian.

"Is everything ready for the bounty when it starts coming in?" asked Sean.

"Yes, I believe it is. When is everyone finished eating, would you three mind meeting me outside to make sure I do not forget something? This is my first time doing this, and I want to ensure I have everything I need."

"Yes, of course, we will," said Sean.

"Okay, I will be outside," she said as she got up and started walking out. But, before she got to the door, she heard someone call her.

"My lady?"

Veronica turned and saw the woman whose husband had insulted her walk up. "Yes?'

"I am sorry to disturb you, but I was wondering about the families who do not have a way to keep the meat?" The woman wouldn't look up at Veronica.

"What is your name?"

"Lilibeth."

"What a beautiful name. How can I help you?"

"Our storeroom was damaged last winter. My husband was hoping to win enough money at the festival games to repair it but only won a small amount."

Veronica realized why the man was so upset at the tavern. She thought for a moment. "Do not worry. I will come up with something to help."

"Please, my husband will be so upset if he found out I told you. He is young and proud. It would hurt him if people found out he could not take care of his family."

"I will be sure he does not know. But do me a favor?"

"What is that, my lady?"

"Would you mind looking at me?"

Lilibeth raised her head and looked at Veronica.

"There, that is better. It will be all right, Lilibeth."

"Thank you," she said with a big smile.

"Please, do not thank me. I wish more people would come to me when they need help. Now, are the ladies ready for a very trying day?"

"Yes, my lady. Everyone is eager to get started. We all said a prayer for a very bountiful hunt."

"Wonderful. I have faith that the good lord will bless us this year. Would you like to go with me to check on everything? Some of the men will meet us outside to ensure I am ready."

"Aye. I would like that."

As they walked out, Veronica asked her about her family. Lilibeth was surprised at how Veronica did not act above her. Instead, she was open and friendly.

Two hours later, a horse pulling a cart full of red deer, squirrels, and pheasants pulled in, and everyone went to work. It was amazing to watch the woman at work together. They did not break until lunch when Veronica ordered them to stop for a few minutes and eat.

Ellis and the first group soon arrived in high spirits, proud of their hunt. Veronica pulled Ellis and Kieran off to the side and told them about the damaged storerooms and how she wanted to help. They both agreed with her plan.

Before the men left the dining hall after eating lunch, she called a meeting.

"Tomorrow night, we will celebrate. The day after, I will need to hire a few men to go and help some of the families repair their storerooms. If you need yours rebuilt or need work, go to Kieran after this afternoon's hunt, for he will be handling this for me. Good luck for the men heading out, and may God bless you as he did this morning."

The men were excited about the repairs and the chance to make money. Veronica needed to thank Lilibeth for telling her about this problem. Hearing them talk, she was amazed at how many needed help. Helping people had become a part of who she was, and losing that would have been hard for her to accept.

"I owe you an apology," said Ellis.

"Why?"

"You know I wanted the other estate because it was closer to my ships, but I also did not want the responsibility that came with this castle. I was being selfish, and I threw all of this on you. I came here to join the hunt and see if you could handle this place. I would have switched our homes if I thought it was too overwhelming for you. But you have handled everything better than I could. It is as if you were raised to be the leader of this place."

Veronica smiled as she thought of her grandfather. He had once told her she was better suited to run that castle. That was why he trained her in everything a leader should know.

But she would never tell Ellis.

"Thank you for seeing that I am meant to be here. I love this place and the people."

"You have won their hearts and respect. You never cease to amaze me. I love you, little sister," said Ellis as he hugged her.

"I love you, too."

As the second group got ready to depart, Veronica walked up to Sean to talk to Liam and Ian.

"I want all of you to be careful and return safe." She looked at Sean and smiled before walking off.

Seinaid watched the action between Veronica and Sean. "All right, when can we talk about you and Sean?"

Veronica grabbed her and pulled her into a room. "You cannot say anything to anybody."

"Okay."

"No, swear."

"I swear."

"We kissed."

Seinaid squealed and jumped up and down, happy.

"Why are you so happy about this?"

"Come on, you and Sean are perfect for each other."

"No, we are not. I cannot be with him. It will not work."

"Why?"

Veronica walked to a chair and sat down. "There is something wrong with me."

"What are you talking about? There is nothing wrong with you."

"He only kissed me because I was upset. I had a weak moment, and he was comforting me. That's all."

"How can someone be so blind?" whispered Seinaid to herself. "Ronnie, I am going to tell you something I am not supposed to." She took a deep breath and looked at Veronica. "Sean is in love with you."

Veronica looked at Seinaid with a blank expression. "Did you hear me?"

"Be serious, Seinaid. This is not the time to be funny."

"I am not trying to be funny. He has loved you for a long time."

"He cannot love me," she said, shaking her head.

"Why?"

"I do not know if I can be with someone again."

"What are you talking about? You are young. wonderful, loving person. Who would not want to be with you?"

"I do not know if I can love anyone again. It is too painful if things go wrong. And I could not hurt Sean that way."

"Why do you think it will go wrong? You have always been such a warm-hearted person."

"Something happened that I did not tell you."

"What?"

"Owen did not come to my bed the night I was married. That night, he went to someone else." Veronica tried to hold back the tears, but just saying it brought back that deep pain.

Seinaid was stunned and stared at Veronica, not knowing what to say. When she saw tears running down her face, she got up and went to her and wrapped her arms around her. Finally, Veronica let go of the pain and sobbed on Seinaid's shoulder.

Once Veronica stopped crying, she sat back from Seinaid and wiped her face. "I have not told anyone what happened except Hannah. Some found out, but I still cannot bring it up without a knife stabbing my heart. I fear loving someone and not being enough for them."

"I am so sorry you had to go through that, but Ronnie, you do notrealize what you have right in front of you. When I said Sean loves you, I meant he is wholeheartedly in love with you. It could be what heals your broken heart."

Veronica looked at Seinaid and thought about that kiss. It felt so good to be in his arms.

"Can you at least think about giving him a chance?"

"Yes, I will think about it. But please do not tell anyone what I told you."

"I swear I will never tell a soul," said Seinaid as she put her hand on her chest.

Veronica smiled and stood, pulling Seinaid up with her.

"It is time to get back and see if they need anything. After that, we should have more kills arriving."

A couple of hours later, Veronica was talking to Angus in the hallway. He was a doctor she had staying at the castle during the hunt. Her grandfather always had one just in case someone was hurt. As they were talking, Beatrice came running in.

"We need you, doctor. Someone has been shot."

When they ran out the doors, Veronica saw Liam jumping down from the front of the cart while Ian was in the back, tending to someone. Angus ran and jumped in the cart and immediately started checking the wounded person.

"We need to get him inside," hollered Angus. Liam and another man grabbed a board and took it to the cart. Once they got the injured man on the board, they slid it off the end, and the men carried him towards the castle. Veronica couldn't see who it was until they reached the doors, and her heart stopped beating when she saw Sean lying on the board. He was covered in blood, pale, and not moving.

Veronica had a room prepared just in case of an emergency. Once they put Sean on the bed, the doctor started working on him. The servants quickly brought hot water and towels into the room.

Veronica climbed up on the other side of the bed and held Sean's hand.

"My lady, I do not think you should watch this," said Angus.

"Do not worry. This is not my first bullet wound. Actually, I have been shot."

"What?" said Ellis as he had just entered the room. She looked over and saw everyone looking at her.

"It is a long story. I will tell you later, but Sean needs our attention right now."

After Angus removed the bullet and stitched him up, he asked Veronica if she wanted to clean him up.

"Yes, of course," she said as she grabbed the towels and put them in hot water. "How is he?" she asked as she cleaned the blood from his chest

"He has lost a lot of blood. He has a chance if he makes it in the next few days. I am sorry."

Tears formed in her eyes as she thought of Sean dying. "Thank you. I know you did your best," said Veronica.

"I will be back to check on him," said Angus as he left the room.

"Ian, Michael, could you change his clothes? He needs out of these."

"Yes," said Ian as he walked over and picked up a gown. Veronica had everything in the room that someone might need. She had never dreamed it would be Sean lying there in that bed.

She walked out with the others to give them time to change him.

"Does someone want to tell me how you were shot?" asked Ellis.

"Not know, Ellis. Get Ian to tell you what happened."

"I can help you."

Veronica turned and saw Murray standing there.

"Who are you?" asked Ellis.

"This is Murray. He saved me that night. I offered him and his wife, Amy, to come here and start a new life."

"Okay, Murray, how about we go and talk."

"I am coming too. This will be interesting," said Kieran.

"It will give my sister some time alone," said Ellis as he hugged her.

After they walked off, she leaned against the wall, closed her eyes, and prayed for Sean.

"Ronnie?" said Seinaid as she and Liam walked up.

"I am sorry I left so quickly. I had to get Sean's blood off me. It never bothered me about blood, but it is Sean's. I could not stand it on me," said Liam, looking pale.

"I understand. The doctor removed the bullet, but he lost a lot of blood. If he makes it in the next couple of days, he has a chance. We need to watch for infection."

"Sean is strong. He will be okay," said Seinaid.

Veronica broke down and started crying. "I cannot lose him," she said as Seinaid held her.

The door opens, and Ian walks out. "He is changed and resting."

"Thank you. Why do you not go and get cleaned up?" said Veronica as she wiped her face.

Ian looked down at his hands and clothes. "I guess I should," he said, then walked away.

"Do you want to come in and see him?"

"Yes. We would like that," said Liam.

They all walked in, went toward the bed, and stared at Sean, not knowing what to say.

"Liam, Michael, is there any way the two of you could handle the rest of today? I want to stay with Sean," said Veronica.

"Yes, I will find Kieran and Ellis and make sure everything is taken care of," said Liam.

"They are with Murray. He is telling them how I got shot."

"I am sorry. You were shot?" asked Seinaid.

"It is a long story. I will tell you later," said Veronica as she walked to the side of the bed and sat down. She took Sean's hand and held it between hers.

"We are going to go," said Seinaid as she walked up to Veronica. She leaned down and moved a stray hair off of Sean's forehead. She then hugged Veronica and whispered in her ear. "Talk to him. Tell him how you feel."

They left the room, and Veronica sat beside Sean, staring at his face.

"Seinaid says you love me. That you have for a long time. Do you want to know something funny? I had feelings for you when we were young. I could not say anything because my father and grandfather would never allow us to be together. So, I put it out of my head, but I did enjoy the kiss. I was back there with you in my heart for a few seconds. And since you cannot hear me, I will admit I would like another kiss. I could not say that if you were awake.

"I know that makes me a coward. If you knew everything that had happened, you would see me differently. You would see me as I do. I am afraid to let anyone in my heart, but I do not know what to do with these feelings I am having now. All I am sure of is that you need to fight. I cannot imagine my life without you in it. I know if you were awake, you would tell me to quit rambling, but I am afraid. Sean, I am so scared." She brought his hand to her cheek and felt how cold it was.

She put his hand down and went to the door. When she opened it, she saw Beatrice sitting in a chair, waiting.

"I need two bed warmers."

"Yes, my lady," said Beatrice as she took off. It wasn't but a couple of minutes, and she was back with the bed warmers. After filling them with embers from the fireplace, they put one at the foot of the bed to warm his feet and the other near his shoulders to warm his body. She then covered him with a heavy blanket and pulled it to his chin.

A little later, she checked him. After a while, she heard a knock at the door. When she opened it, she saw Ian.

"Everyone has returned, and they are asking about Sean."

"Beatrice, stay with Sean. If anything changes, come get me."

"Yes, my lady."

After she walked out, she stopped. "Ian, what happened out there? How did Sean get shot?"

"We were walking around when we heard a shot. We did not even see the deer. The bullet went through its neck and hit Sean. It was an accident."

"Does everyone know about Sean?"

"Yes, they are wondering how he is."

"Okay, let us go."

When they walked into the dining room, everyone grew quiet.

"Sean is alive and holding on. I hope you will keep him in your prayers. I know Sean would want everything to continue as it should. Kieran, have you made arrangements for the storeroom repairs?"

"Yes, I have enough workers and a list of all that needs repairing."

"Good, so tonight, I want everyone to relax and celebrate a successful hunt. I know everyone is worried about Sean, but he is strong. There would be hell to pay if he found out we sat around worrying about him. Most of you know Sean, and you know I am right."

"Aye," said several men.

"So, tonight, I need you all to celebrate for him and yourselves. Celebrate with your families and have plenty to eat this winter. Celebrate for Sean, for me."

"Aye," said the crowd, and the celebration started as a line of servants brought in the food.

Veronica had gone all out with this celebration, and even though she would not join them, she wanted everyone to have plenty to eat and drink.

When Veronica left the party, she returned to Sean's room, where she found the doctor examining him.

"How is he?"

"He is hanging in there. It was wise of you to keep him warm. His breathing is shallow but steady. He will have a fighting chance if he can hang on for a day or two. We will need to watch for infection."

Veronica stayed in the room with Sean for two days. She would curl beside him to sleep but would wake up at night to check if he was still breathing.

On the second day, Sean slowly opened his eyes. It took a few seconds to focus and realize he was in a bed. He was too weak to move his arms. He then felt something move beside him. He looked to his right and saw blonde hair sticking out from under a blanket.

"Ron...Ronnie?" he said barely above a whisper. His throat was so dry and painful.

Her head popped up, and her eyes were wide. "Sean?" she said as she jumped up, causing him to grunt in pain. "Oh, I am sorry," she said, growing still. "Is there anything I can get you?"

"Water," he whispered.

She slowly got off the bed, trying not to cause him more pain. She went to the door to find someone to help raise him to drink water. When she opened the door, she was surprised to see people lying on blankets. Kieran, Ian, Michael, and Ellis lay on the floor.

Hearing the door opened, Kieran woke up.

"He is awake," she said, waking up the rest of them. "I need your help. He needs water."

Everyone got up and came inside the room.

"Hey, brother. I thought I had lost you," said Kieran as he walked up to Sean's side of the bed.

"Ronnie, grab that pillow. When I lift him, put it under his head," said Kieran as he leaned down. When Veronica was ready with the pillow, Kieran slowly lifted him, and Veronica slipped the pillow under his head. She then went and poured him a glass of water. He slowly sipped the water until it was gone.

"Hi," said Sean, making everyone laugh. The tension they had felt left their bodies with one single word.

"We arc so glad you are awake," said Ellis.

Sean smiled as he looked at everyone. He then looked down and saw Veronica had climbed up in the bed and was holding his hand. She was looking at him with a big smile on her face. He thought he saw love in her eyes, but it was probably only a wishful fantasy.

"How long have I been asleep?" he asked, not taking his eyes off her.

"Two days. Could someone go get the doctor?" she said, not taking her eyes off Sean.

"I will," said Kieran as he left the room.

While he was gone, they filled Sean in on everyone he had missed. Mainly all the antics that happened at the celebration, and the wives had to come and treat them like children. Several got way too into things, Sean couldn't help but laugh even though it hurt. Veronica could not stop smiling as she watched him.

It was only a short time till Kieran returned with the doctor.

"It is good to see you awake, Mr. McCloud."

"It is good to be awake," he said, smiling.

"Now, let us look and see how you are healing."

Everyone grew quiet as they watched the doctor check his wound.

"Well, so far, it looks good. No infection, but you have lost much blood, and it will take some time to get your strength back. So, I order two weeks of bed rest."

"Two weeks? I cannot lay up for two weeks." Sean looked down with a frown.

"Stop pouting. The doctor said two weeks, so it is two weeks," said Veronica sternly.

"Well, I do believe you are in good hands. I will be back later to check on you," said the doctor, chuckling as he left the room.

"Since you are doing better, I need to check on the repairs. I will be back in a day or two," said Kieran.

"Okay, let me know if you need anything," said Veronica.

"Could you use any more help?" asked Ian.

"Aye. If it is you, I already have several that do not know the first thing about building."

"Me too," said Michael.

"All right, let us go. At least now it will get done sooner."

After the guys left, Ellis walked up to the bed. "Sean, I know it will be hard for you to stay in bed, but you must listen to Veronica. All right?"

"Aye. I will do as told," said Sean, smiling at Veronica.

"Ronnie, will you walk me out? I need to talk to you before I leave."

"All right."

Veronica left the room and walked towards the stairs. "Are you leaving?'

"Yes. Now that Sean is awake and seems to be getting better, I want you to know I approve of you and him."

"What?"

"I can see the love you two have for each other," said Ellis as he stopped walking and turned to face her.

"I do not know what you are talking about. There is nothing between Sean and me but friendship."

"Ronnie, you might not want to see it, but that man loves you, and I think if you are honest with yourself, you will realize you have feelings for him. I know that Father would have said no before, but since Owen, he only wants you happy."

"I do not know if I can."

Ellis looked at her and saw so much sadness. "Ronnie, do not give up on love, and do not waste a chance when it is right in front of you." Ellis kissed her forehead, then turned and walked up the stairs.

Veronica watched him walk away, noticing a sadness she had never seen in him before. She decided to go to her room and freshen up since Sean was doing better and needed to be with Leah for more than just feeding. It somehow calmed her thoughts to have her little girl in her arms. Sending Beatrice to watch over Sean eased her mind so she would have time to think.

Should she risk her heart again? Could she survive another failed relationship? Would Sean love her forever or replace her with someone else? Such things went through her head as she soaked in her bathwater, Leah asleep in the bed.

She had never felt more lost and unsure of what to do in her whole life.

# Chapter
# Twenty-Eight

Life is full of happiness
and tears; be strong
and have faith.

Kareena Kapoor Khan

Veronica returned to Sean's room to find him sleeping. Beatrice was sitting by the bed, watching him sleep.

"How long has he been sleeping?" she whispered as she approached Beatrice.

"Ever since I arrived."

"I am awake," said Sean as he opened his eyes.

"Beatrice, will you go see if the broth is ready?"

"Aye, my lady."

"I had some bone broth prepared," said Veronica as she sat beside him.

"I think I am hungry."

"You think?"

"I do not feel much but the burning in my belly."

"Do you need something for the pain?"

"No, I want to stay awake." He looked at Veronica, and he could tell something was wrong. She would not look him in the eye as she had before she left earlier. "Ronnie, what is wrong?"

She looked at him and then looked away, took a deep breath, and let it out. "I do not want things to change between us. I could not stand losing you as a friend."

"Why would you lose me?"

She was scared to say anything but had to be brave and give things a chance. "Do you love me?" She closed her eyes and prayed she did not just make a mistake.

He reached over and placed his hand on her arm. He wanted to touch her face, but he still didn't have the strength to raise his arm that high. "Ronnie, look at me."

She slowly turned her head and opened her eyes. He could see the fear in them, and it made his heart hurt seeing her like that.

"I have loved you as far back as I can remember. I never said anything because I did not deserve you, and I knew they would never let me be with you. My heart died a little when you married Owen, but I thought you would be happy."

Tears glistened in her eyes as she looked at Sean. "What if I told you I wanted to try and be with someone again, but I am scared?"

"I know you have been hurt, but give me a chance, and I will mend that wee heart of yours."

"What if we take things slow?"

"How slow?" Sean asked with a slight smile.

"I do not know. Maybe, we could start with some kissing." She looked away as her cheeks turned red.

"I would like that. How about we start now?"

When Veronica looked back, he had a big smile on his face. She leaned down towards him and lightly touched his lips with hers. She sat up quickly, gaining a frown from Sean.

"That will do for now. You need to rest and heal." She heard a knock on the door. "Come in."

Beatrice came in, carrying a bowl. She walked over and handed it to Veronica.

"Can you sit up, or do you need help?"

Sean slowly pushed himself up and waited for Veronica to start feeding him. He couldn't believe he had a chance to be with the love of his life.

A month went by, and Sean had healed completely. He and Veronica spent as much time together as possible, and love grew in Veronica's heart. Finally, it was time for Veronica's family and Owen's to come for Christmas.

Sean was worried that Henry would disapprove of them being together. Veronica tried to ease his worry, but the fear of having to let her go tore his heart out.

When everyone finally arrived, the first thing Owen did was go and pick up his little girl. Leah looked at Owen and planted her little hands on his face as if she remembered him. Tears welled in everyone's eyes as they watched the reunion between them. Veronica noticed Owen had lost weight and lacked the vibrance he had once had. She walked up to him and smiled as Leah made baby noises as if she was talking to him.

"How have you been?" she asked.

"I am better," he said, holding Leah close and looking toward Veronica. "I have missed her," he said, kissing Leah's forehead.

"You intend on staying for a while?"

"Yes, for a couple of months. Is that all right with you?"

"Yes," she said, smiling. "You need to spend as much time as possible with your little girl." Veronica wanted to make sure Owen knew Leah would always be his in her eyes so he wouldn't feel threatened when it came out about her and Sean.

"Thank you," he said, smiling back at her.

Henry walked up and wrapped his arm around Veronica. "But you will have to share her with the grandparents."

"Of course, a little," said Owen.

"Look, boy, you will not monopolize all her time," said Callum as he walked up beside Owen.

"I will leave you all to figure this out," said Veronica as she walked over to where the women stood, talking.

"I expect you to have decorated already," said Dinah.

"And leave you out of helping?" said Veronica.

"Oh, when can we start?" asked Dinah, excited.

"Tomorrow," said Veronica, not expecting Dinah to grab her in a hug. She then pushed Veronica away as if something had just hit her. "Is Hannah coming?"

"No, not this year. But Lydia and Adrian are, and Liam and Seinaid also."

"Excellent. The more, the merrier. We need to fill this castle with so much joy," said Dinah as she walked around, looking at doorways and walls and pointing out where things should go.

"She's going to be a handful. Decorating is all she has talked about since we told her we were coming here for Christmas," said Ann as she shook her hand.

"That is just fine. If she wants to do most of the work, I will not stand in her way," said Veronica, smiling as she watched Dinah talk about what would go where.

A few days went by before Sean made an appearance.

"I was beginning to think you had lost your courage and decided I was not worth it," said Veronica as she crossed her arms over her chest.

"Never," said Sean smiling. Veronica could never stay mad at him when he gave her that devilish handsome smile, and he knew it.

"Do not do that. I want to stay mad at you. I thought you decided not to come," she said, pouting.

"I love you and would never do that. I was helping Kieran at his place. Liam helped him get a farm," he said as he wrapped his arms around her.

"I heard that. Is it a good place?" she said as she snuggled into his chest.

"Aye, it is a large plot of land. It even has a couple of tenants' homes. So that is what I was helping with."

"All right, I forgive you for not sending word so I would not worry." Sean had a good excuse, but she wasn't letting him off that easy.

"Okay, okay. I should have sent word."

"I forgive you. We are about to eat supper. You want to join us?"

"No. I came here straight from Kieran's. I need a bath."

"Your room is ready for you. I will send some hot water up."

"Thank you, sweet lass," he said, kissing her quickly. Then he let her go and took the stairs two at a time.

She smiled as she watches him, then turned around and saw Dinah standing there with her head tilted to the side, smiling.

"Is that how you are so good at discovering people's secrets?" asked Veronica.

"What?"

"You are like a ghost. Nobody can hear you walk up behind them. Why are you standing there?"

"You and Sean?" asked Dinah.

"Yes. But do not say anything. Sean wants to talk to my father first."

"Okay, I will not say anything, But I want details as soon as possible." Dinah wrapped her arm in Veronica's and walked into the dining room, where everyone was waiting.

"Who was it?" asked Henry.

"It was Sean," said Veronica as she sat down.

"How is he doing? Ellis told me about the hunt and Sean getting shot."

"Sean was shot, and what is the hunt?" asked Owen.

"The hunt was something my grandfather would have every year. All the neighboring families would come here, and the men would hunt for the day while the women process what they bring in. It is then divided between all the families, so everyone has enough to make it through the winter."

"That is a splendid idea," said Callum.

"Yes, it was the first time I held it by myself. It was going great until Sean got shot. Grandfather always had a doctor present when the hunt was going on in case something happened, and I am glad I also did."

"That was a wise decision," said Callum.

"How is Sean?" asked Owen.

"Doing really well."

Ellen watched and listened, noticing a light in Veronica's eyes when discussing Sean. It would be good to find happiness there, and Sean was a good man. Ellen worried about what Henry would say. He wouldn't accept just anybody with Veronica after what happened with Owen. Henry was going to be more protective than ever.

After supper, everyone retired to the game room. Veronica entered with Leah after feeding and changing her napkins and clothes. The grandparents were at a table playing cards.

Owen and Dinah were sitting on the couch talking when they saw her.

"I get her," said Owen as he stood and held out his hands. Leah reached for him, and Owen smiled big. "That is my girl," he said as he took her.

Sean walked in, dressed in new beige britches and a loose-fitting red shirt that laced up the front. Sean looked like one of those pirates Veronica had read about: his muscular body, confident stride, and windblown hair. Veronica had to look away before they all noticed how he had affected her. She had never believed she would react like a woman in those books, but she wanted Sean.

He walked over to where Veronica stood.

"Hi, Sean. I heard about your mishap at the hunt. So glad you are doing good," said Owen as he sat down and started playing with Leah.

"Aye, me too. Good to see you again, Dinah."

"You too," she replied, smiling between him and Veronica.

"Sean, come over here and tell us your harrowing brush with death," said Henry as he waved Sean over.

Sean laughed and walked over, sitting between Henry and Callum at the table.

"You remember Lord Pierce?" Henry said as he played a card.

"Aye, we met at the wedding."

"Good to see you up and walking around," said Callum.

Sean told the story of that horrible day he was shot, or what he remembered. He apologized that it wasn't more interesting because once he passed out, he knew nothing until he woke up in bed.

"What were the chances a bullet would go through the deer and hit you?" said Henry.

"Aye. I would not have believed it if it had not happened to me."

Once the game was finished, Callum stood. "I am going to steal my grandbaby away from my son."

"Lord Aldridge, may I have a private word?" Sean asked.

"Certainly. Ladies, if you will excuse us for a moment," said Henry as he stood. Sean bowed to the women before he followed Henry out of the room. "Let us go to the library," said Henry as they walked down the hall.

Once they entered, Henry sat behind the desk, and Owen sat in a chair in front of the desk.

"What did you want to talk about?"

"I want to marry Veronica."

Henry did not move or act surprised. "Ellis has already spoken to me about you. He thought there was something between you two." He was quiet for a second, then leaned forward and rested his elbows on the desk. "You would become a wealthy man marrying Veronica."

Sean tensed when he heard that. "If I wanted money, I would go to my grandfather. I would even receive a title from him."

"Your grandfather?"

"Aye, Balfour McDonald."

"Lord Balfour of the highlands?" asked Henry, surprised.

"Aye, he is my grandfather."

"Then why are you living as a tenant?"

"My father met my mother when he traveled here for business. They fell in love, but Balfour refused to let em marry. He had plans for my father to marry a neighboring clan's daughter."

"So, your father left everything behind for your mother."

"Aye. I did not know anything about it until Balfour showed up at my home two years ago. He wanted my father to go back and take over the clan. He said no, so Balfour asked me to go. I said no at first, but I went last year for a while."

"Last year? After Veronica was married?"

"Aye. If I wanted money, I could have it."

"Why did you not take him up on the offer?"

"That was not my home. I have an aunt who had a passel of bairns. One of them could take over. My father needed me more than he did."

Henry watched him, not saying anything.

"I have loved Veronica for most of my life. I knew you and Lord Brannon would never allow me to marry her, so I never said anything."

"My daughter has been hurt very badly. I do not want to make another decision that would cause her more pain. So, this time, I will consider her point of view, and if I know my daughter, she is standing outside the door. Let her in if you do not mind, and I will talk to her."

Sean got up and opened the door, finding Veronica with her ear pressed to the door. She stumbled, and Sean caught her. Looking up, she saw him smiling down at her, and her father chuckled.

"Come in, Ronnie, and shut the door." She walked in, watching Sean as he shut the door, still smiling at her. Then she walked over and sat down, looking at her father, nervous.

"He wants to marry you."

"He loves me," she said, smiling.

Henry was so relieved to see a smile on her face. "How do you feel about him?"

"When I was younger, I liked him, but like Sean, I knew you would never approve. When I am with him, I feel safe. I do not know how to explain it, but I feel happy. I loved Owen, and I felt nothing but pain when everything happened. I do not feel any pain when I am with Sean."

Henry grew sad, and he looked down. "I am so sorry. You were hurt because of me. I should have known."

"Do not blame yourself. There is no way you could have known."

"You had been out in society for two years, and Owen had shown no interest. Then when his family was in dire straits, he came calling."

"Him wanting my dowry was not a secret. Father, you had no way of knowing their plan."

"I knew what Agnes was capable of. I was so happy someone like Owen would be in your life. I thought he would protect you. But, even if I did not know about Agnes, I still failed as your father. I did not see the pain you were in. You have always been so strong that I did not pay attention. It was not until after they told me that I saw how you were hurting."

Veronica lowered her head. "I am not strong. I would have ignored the pain and stayed married if I had been. I would have been a good wife and hid how I felt, but instead, I brought shame to you." Tears flowed from her eyes as she spoke.

Henry got up, walked to her, and kneeled, taking her hands. "Ronnie, you have never brought shame to your family or me. You are my most treasured child. You have only made me proud."

She looked up and saw nothing but love in her father's eyes.

"Do you love Sean?"

"Yes, dad, I do."

"Then, if you want my blessing, you have it."

She reached and wrapped her arms around his neck and hugged him. "Thank you," she said in a whisper.

"Now, go see your young man and tell him the news," said Henry as he stood, pulling her up with them.

She wiped her face as she walked towards the door but stoppeds and turneds her head back, giving him a big smile. "You have made me happy," she said, then left the room.

Henry sat down in the chair and lowered his head. "God, please let her be happy," he whispered.

Veronica was running down the hall when she found Sean leaning against the railing at the stairs. He turned and saw her running towards him. She stopped only a foot away and stared up at him with tears. He held his breath, afraid he was going to lose her.

"He said yes."

Sean picked her up and spun as they laughed. He set her down and kissed her soundly on the lips. She quickly pulled back and looked around, afraid someone might see them.

"We cannot do that. If my father sees us, he might change his mind."

"I do not care. You are mine, and I am never letting you go."

Veronica looked into his eyes and saw so much love.

"How soon can we be married?" asked Sean, holding her close and resting his chin on her head.

"Sean, I have only been divorced for three months. I would prefer not to cause any more scandal than I have already. I cannot do that to my parents. You do understand?"

"Aye, I do. But does that mean we cannot be together for a while?" he asked, pulling his head back and looking down at her.

"No, I do not want us to be separated. I want you here as much as possible. I cannot imagine you not with me."

"Did your father say yes?"

They both turned around and saw Dinah standing there with a big grin.

"Aye, he did," said Sean.

Dinah ran and hugged them both. "I'm so happy for you."

"Sean, will you give me a moment with her?"

"Aye, I am going to go to bed. I am tired from helping Kieran today. See you tomorrow." He brought her back in for a hug and quickly kissed her before she could object. He went toward his room feeling happier than he has been in a long time.

"You are so lucky," said Dinah as she watched Sean walk away.

"I know. He loves me."

"You never believed someone could love you when nobody in this world deserves love more than you," said Dinah, looking at Veronica.

"How is Owen?"

"He is doing better, attending some social functions when Ellis is in town. I was worried about him for a while, but he has come a long way."

"What do you think he will say about Sean and me?"

"I am happy for you."

They both jumped, not expecting anybody to be behind them. When they looked back, they saw Owen standing there.

"You are just as quiet as your sister," said Veronica as she put her hand on her chest, feeling her heart racing.

"Sorry if I scared you," he said, chuckling. He walked up to them and smiled at Veronica. "I am truly happy for you and Sean. You deserve someone who will be devoted. I believe he loves you with everything he has. Like I should have done from the beginning."

"Thank you, Owen. That means so much to me."

"I am off to bed. I lost Leah to her grandparents, but come tomorrow, she is mine again," he said as he went up the stairs to his room. The thought of Veronica being with someone else still stung, but he had accepted that they were over. He still had his little girl to love, and that was all he needed.

Six months later, Veronica stood at the church doorway, getting married to Sean. The church once against was packed with family, friends, and most of the town. She saw Sean and Kieran standing beside the vicar, wearing their kilts and clan tartans across their chest. Veronica wore an off-the-shoulder navy blue dress with dark red embroidery on the collar, cuffs, and hem. It wasn't as extravagant as her first, but regal looking all the same. A gold tiara with a large ruby in the center sat on her head. She wore her hair down, letting her curls free. Across her chess were both the Brannon and McDonald tartan in a crisscross fashion, which was custom when two important clans married.

The knowledge of Sean being Lord McDonald's grandson was revealed when Balfour made a surprise visit. He was mad at Sean for refusing his offer but got over his anger when he heard of the engagement. His grandson marrying Veronica of Blackthorn made him proud, as if he had a right to be proud. Sean was not happy with his grandfather and did not like nor trust any of the people in that family.

Before they started walking down the aisle, Veronica leaned over and whispered in her father's ear, causing Henry to cough.

"Let us get you married before I challenge him with pistols at dawn," said Henry, causing Veronica to laugh.

As they walk down the aisle, she saw Lydia and Adrian, and Owen brought everyone from her old home in London. When Sean reached to take Veronica's hand, he noticed Henry glaring at him. He looked back at Veronica with a questioning look. Before she could say anything, they heard a loud "DA DA", and she turned around and saw Leah standing on Owen's lap, playfully hitting his face.

"Her first words," said Veronica, loud enough for everyone to hear, causing the crowd to chuckle. Owen was smiling with pride as he held Leah close.

"It was supposed to be uncle," said Ellis, as he tickled her, making Leah squeal and try to hide in Owen's shoulder.

"Humm," said the vicar, trying to get everyone's attention as he glared at Ellis.

"Sorry," said Ellis, as he stopped messing with Leah.

Veronica couldn't help but laugh seeing Ellis in trouble. She looked back at Sean and saw him smiling.

"You sure you want to marry me?"

"With all my heart."

There was not a soul there that could not see the love they had for each other.

After the ceremony was over, Veronica and Sean were in the carriage on their way to the castle. She was leaning against him, his arms wrapped around her.

"Oh, why was your father looking like he wanted strangle me?"

"I told him he was going to be a grandfather again," she said calmly. Sean froze as what she said registered. He then turned her around to face him.

"Is it true? Are you having my bairn?"

"Aye," she said, smiling at him.

He looked at her with so much love. "I love you so much." He then kissed her with all the love he felt.

Veronica finally had the love and family she had always wanted. Her once broken heart was now whole.

In a rundown house, an older woman and two little girls, barely three, were shoved into a room. The woman huddled in the corner holding the children close. It wasn't long, and the door opened, and three men walked in. Fear gripped the woman as she recognized the man standing before her, Feagin Parnell.

"You are the woman that used to run the orphanage on King's Road. I want to know who you were contacting to steal my people?"

"I do not know what you are talking about."

Feagin walked over and picked the woman up from the floor by her throat. "I am not a patient man. You will tell me what I want to know, or you will die." He let her go when he heard the children crying. He kneeled and touched the girl's head.

"Are you not a beauty." He then stood and smiled at the woman. "I do not deal in children, but Blakely would love having these two. He would make a good amount selling them."

"No, please, do not hurt them. Let them go back home," said the woman as tears fell. She went to the floor, pulling the children to her.

"Tell me what I want to know, and I will have the children returned." He walked a few steps back.

"Swear you will return them to the orphanage unharmed," said the woman with more courage than she felt.

"Why would that matter if I swear or not?"

"If you break your word, what will your men think? Even a man like yourself needs the trust of his men."

Feagin looked over at his men and noticed them looking away. He looked back at the woman and smiled, knowing he had to keep his word. He didn't intend to hurt the children anyway.

"Fine, Gregory, take the children back to the orphanage unharmed," he said, pulling a chair from the corner and sitting right in front of her.

Gregory walked over and kneeled. "I promise they will be returned unharmed," he said as he held his hands out for the children to take.

"Girls, go with this man. He is going to take you back home. I know the other children are probably sad because they have not gotten to play with you two," she said, trying to ease their minds about going without her.

"Will we see you there?" asked one of the girls.

"Yes, of course," she said, trying to smile, knowing she would never leave there alive.

"Who were you working for? What was his name?" he asked after they were gone.

The woman closed her eyes and lowered her head. "God, forgive me," she whispered. "It was not a man," she said, not looking up.

"What did you say?" Feagin wasn't sure he heard her right.

She raised her head as tears stream down her face. "It was not a man."

Feagin stared at her, trying to see if she was lying. He leaned forward. "Tell me everything."

Milton Keynes UK
Ingram Content Group UK Ltd.
UKHW020945280923
429557UK00014B/575